PLANETS

LIFE SCIENCE LIBRARY

PLANETS

by Carl Sagan, Jonathan Norton Leonard
and the Editors of TIME-LIFE BOOKS

CONSULTING EDITORS
René Dubos
Henry Margenau
C. P. Snow

TIME-LIFE INTERNATIONAL (NEDERLAND) N.V.

ABOUT THIS BOOK

THE SPACE AGE has given new impetus both to man's curiosity about the planets and to his need to know more about them. The techniques of modern astronomy are expanding knowledge about the planets at an accelerating rate, and the day is approaching when man will visit other planets.

This book discusses, among other things, the many broad areas of disagreement that exist among astronomers regarding the planets' origin, composition, atmospheres and surfaces. It is concerned particularly with the possibility of life—no matter how primitive it may be—on other planets.

The text chapters are accompanied by picture essays, which are designed to be read independently or with the text. For example, Chapter 1, "The Discovery of the Solar System", surveys the evolution of man's thinking about the planets, while the picture essay, "Solving the Riddle of the Heavens", analyses the changing concepts of the solar system.

THE AUTHORS

CARL SAGAN, a leading astronomer, is Director of the Laboratory for Planetary Studies at Cornell University and a staff member of the Smithsonian Institution's Astrophysical Observatory. He is also Editor of *Icarus: International Journal of the Solar System,* and special consultant to the National Aeronautics and Space Administration and the National Academy of Sciences. He is co-author of the book *Intelligent Life in the Universe.*

JONATHAN NORTON LEONARD is a free-lance writer and a former staff writer of TIME-LIFE BOOKS who has specialized for most of his life in technical and scientific subjects. For 20 years he was Science Editor of TIME, covering everything from the first atomic explosion to the latest developments in biology and electronics. He has written many books, the most recent of which are *Flight into Space* and *Exploring Science.*

THE CONSULTING EDITORS

RENÉ DUBOS, a member and Emeritus Professor of The Rockefeller University, is a distinguished microbiologist and experimental pathologist who was awarded the Arches of Science Award in 1966 and the Pulitzer Prize in 1969 for his book *So Human an Animal: How We Are Shaped by Surroundings and Events.* He is also the author of *Mirage of Health* and *Man Adapting* and co-author of *Health and Disease* in this series.

HENRY MARGENAU is Eugene Hig-

gins Emeritus Professor of Physics and Natural Philosophy at Yale, and an authority in spectroscopy and nuclear physics. He wrote *Open Vistas* and *The Nature of Physical Reality,* and is co-author of *The Scientist* in this series.

C. P. SNOW has won an international audience for his novels, including *The New Men, The Affair* and *Corridors of Power,* which explore the effects of science on today's society.

This international edition adapted by E. W. C. Wilkins.

CONTENTS

PREFACE

This is a timely book. Until recently, the Moon and planets were regarded as being of academic interest only; they fascinated astronomers, both professional and amateur, but studies of them did little to affect our everyday life. Problems such as those of the lunar craters, the rotation of Venus and the polar caps of Mars were of little importance to non-scientists.

The situation today is very different. We are living in the Space Age; rockets have been sent to the Moon and nearer planets, and the first manned voyage to another world cannot lie far ahead. Small wonder, then, that everything possible is being done to find out what our neighbour planets are really like—and small wonder, too, that almost everyone in the modern world takes a lively interest in them.

Moreover, there is the question of "life elsewhere". Now that we know our Earth to be a junior member of an unimportant Solar System it is pure conceit to suppose that our civilization must be unique; much more probably we represent a comparatively primitive stage, and there must surely be many races in the Universe who surpass us. The prospects for intelligent life on the other planets of the Sun's family are admittedly remote, but not until we have a really good knowledge of these worlds can we make reliable guesses as to what may lie beyond. There is, too, the chance that totally alien life-forms may exist.

Many books at non-technical level have been produced of late, but not many combine a full, reliable and up-to-date text with illustrations which are spectacular and well-chosen. The present book by Dr. Sagan and his colleagues does so: it is thought-provoking as well as informative, and I am confident that those who read it will enjoy it as much as I have done.

—Patrick Moore
Director, Armagh Planetarium

1

The Discovery of the Solar System

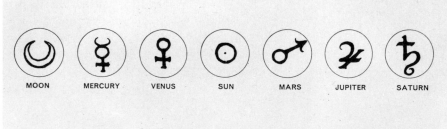

| MOON | MERCURY | VENUS | SUN | MARS | JUPITER | SATURN |

The members of the solar system are personified in this 17th-century German engraving.

ALL MODERN CIVILIZED PEOPLE know, or at least have been taught, that the solar system is a group of nine planets, four of them much larger than the earth, held together by the gravitation of the sun in the centre. The system is at least 10,000 million miles in diameter, a distance hard to imagine but much smaller than the distance to the nearest star, which is 25 million million miles. Astronomers still disagree about how it was formed. Apparently it is about 5,000 million years old and reached its present state not long after the sun condensed out of a great cloud of dust and gas.

This now-familiar picture is highly sophisticated, the product of thousands of years of human observation and thought. It is far from any commonsense conclusion that an intelligent but uninformed man could reach by viewing the heavens with his own eyes. For people who lived before the dawn of history, there was no such thing as a solar system. The world, as they understood it, was a small patch of land bounded by distant hills and perhaps by the blue line of the sea. Close overhead was the sky, and across it rode the beneficent sun, a god giving light and warmth. The moon was a lesser god shining with paler light, and with it at night rode the brilliant innumerable stars. Outside this little universe lay unimagined mystery.

But as human thought grew and improved, it gradually acquired the quality of wonder. A few inquiring minds began to speculate about the drama of the sky. Why did the sun rise at different places? Why did the moon change its shape and sometimes shine wanly by day? Why did a few of the stars—planets—move among the others? Did such things have causes? Did they have meanings for men?

The first astronomers watched the sky and made crude observations. They numbered the days between full moons, and the days in a year. So started an ambitious programme of scientific research: the attempt to understand the solar system. It continued for thousands of years, brought practical benefits and intellectual triumphs, caused furious controversies and repeatedly changed man's view of his place in the universe.

The ancient research programme is not completed yet, though the solar system has grown enormously in men's eyes, both in size and in interest. Recently the pace of discovery has gathered speed and it is approaching a climax. Space ships with delicate instruments are exploring the planets. Men have actually landed on the moon and brought back samples of its rocks and dust.

Both instruments and human explorers are sure to find many surprises, but the greatest prize they seek is life beyond the earth. Most scientists agree that life will appear spontaneously in any place where conditions remain sufficiently favourable for a very long time, but this conviction is based on inferences and extrapolations. They do not know just what conditions are necessary to give birth to living organisms. Some think that the laws of chemistry and physics permit only one broad kind of life. If this is true, all living things that may be found anywhere in the universe will be in a chemical sense distant relatives of man, descended from the same kinds of complex molecules. Made of the same materials and initiated in similar environments, extraterrestrial organisms may be roughly similar to life on earth, in chemistry if not in form. Another view is that many different sets of conditions can produce life, and all such utterly alien organisms will be man's relatives only in the sense that they are alive.

The exploration of the solar system will not answer all questions that can be asked about life, but the first trace of any living organism—or of life now extinct—found on the moon or a planet will cause the highest excitement in the history of science, and the research problem started so long ago will have changed once again man's view of his place in the universe.

This book will sketch briefly the history of the solar system as it grew and took shape in man's understanding and will give the latest information and theories about it, with special emphasis on the planets as places, each with its own characteristics such as surface features, atmosphere, temperature and internal conditions. Each of the nine known planets has its history, which may cast light on the general evolution of planets from the time of their original formation. The moon and other planetary satellites will be included, but the sun will not be described except as a source of light, heat, gravitation and charged particles. Some theories will be presented that seem unlikely at first glance. To consider such theories is only prudence. In astronomy unlikely theories have often proved correct while the commonsense views, including those of genuine experts, have often proved wrong.

The ancients' earth-centred universe

For centuries educated people have known that the sun is by far the largest member of the solar system and stands near its centre. Around it the nine planets are arranged in the following order: Mercury, Venus, Earth, Mars, Jupiter, Saturn, Uranus, Neptune and Pluto. But to the first truly civilized men—such as the ancient Egyptians and Mesopotamians, who were just as intelligent as modern men—the earth appeared flat and solid, and obviously the principal thing in the universe. They knew no reason to think otherwise. They accepted the sun, moon, planets and stars for what they looked like and used their motions as a valuable means of predicting the future.

Prediction of this kind had a successful history. Long before the invention of writing, astronomer-priests kept track of the sun's annual north-and-south motion and connected it correctly with the progress of the seasons on the earth. The priests watched the sun, counted the days after its farthest retreat towards the south and predicted, as if a dependable god had told them, when life-giving floods would sweep down the rivers.

The system worked because floods depend on the seasons, which in turn depend on the sun. The earth's axis of rotation points in such a way that as the earth sweeps around its orbit, each hemisphere, north or south, gets more than its share of sunlight for six months, causing the

THE EGYPTIAN COSMOS was encompassed by the sky goddess Nut, the star-studded figure at the top: early Egyptians believed she swallowed the sun each evening and returned it each morning. Beneath Nut is Shu, the god of air, shown holding symbols of immortality in his hands, and under him lies the earth god Geb, his body covered with leaves. The boats on each side of the drawing carried the sun on its journey across the sky.

alternation from summer to winter. Relating the ocean tides to the moon's apparent changes of shape worked well too, because the moon through its gravitational pull is really the principal cause of the tides. So it was only natural for the astronomer-priests to become convinced that the five "stray sheep"—the visible planets Mercury, Venus, Mars, Jupiter and Saturn—that move in relation to the other stars also had power over earthly affairs. If the sun could bring summer and winter and the moon move the oceans, why shouldn't Mars and Venus have effects on lesser matters such as human wars?

Astrology: predictions from the planets

Out of this wrong but natural conviction grew astrology, the prediction of the future by means of the stars. For astrologers, "the stars" meant principally the planets, the real stars acting as a background. To perform their duties properly the astrologers wanted to know the positions of the planets at specified times in the past and future. This called for careful observation and faithful record-keeping. The best work was done in Mesopotamia, where astronomical records were kept with surprising accuracy as long as 4,000 years ago. Since most events in the heavens repeat themselves, the astrologers could tell by consulting their records where the planets would be when a king planned to launch an attack on a neighbouring State. If they decided that the position of Saturn or Mars—the war planets—would be unfavourable, they might advise the king to hold off until the prospects improved.

This sort of counselling gave the astrologers great economic and political power. Their importance reached its peak in Babylonia 1,000 years before the birth of Christ, where they formed a noble caste whose members had to be physically unblemished and of pure-blooded ancestry. The influence of these haughty aristocrats of mysterious learning reached throughout the ancient world. They are mentioned frequently in the Bible. The Three Wise Men of the East who were led to Bethlehem by a star were almost surely astrologers from Mesopotamia, and the gold, frankincense and myrrh they brought for the infant Jesus were meant at the time to be understood as a sign that they believed the birth to be a great event.

The astrologers learned to forecast lunar and solar eclipses, which were considered important omens. They used only their records and had no notion of the way that the earth casts its shadow on the moon, or the moon passes between the earth and the sun. Explanations of such matters were left for the Greeks, who were the first to progress beyond incurious observation and seek rational explanation.

The Greeks wasted little effort on astrology and as early as 600 B.C. were showing a novel distaste for easy reliance on the supernatural. Greek astronomers believed that the true nature of the heavenly bodies could be revealed by imagining mechanisms that would make them move as they appear to do. In modern scientific jargon this is called "constructing a model". It can be done badly, and the Greeks' models were bad by

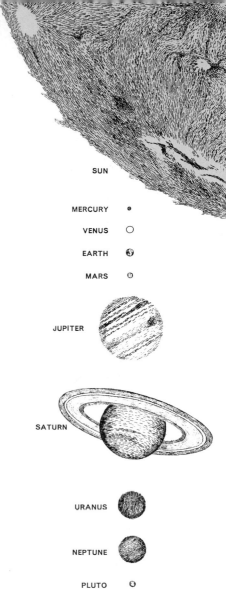

SUN

MERCURY

VENUS

EARTH

MARS

JUPITER

SATURN

URANUS

NEPTUNE

PLUTO

THE RELATIVE SIZES of the planets are illustrated here. Mercury, Venus, Earth and Mars, the four closest to the sun, are called terrestrial, or earth-like, planets, because of their similarity in size and density. The next four planets—Jupiter, Saturn, Uranus and Neptune—are classed as Jovian, or Jupiter-like. While they are much larger than the terrestrial planets, their densities are considerably less. Little is known about Pluto, the most distant of the planets, but it is thought to be terrestrial.

modern standards, but it is a legitimate and often very effective scientific approach.

Most of the models the Greeks constructed to explain the solar system held that the sun, moon, planets and stars are kept from falling by invisible, concentric spheres or circles that rotate and carry them round the earth at different speeds. For reasons that do not impress modern minds, the Greeks admired spheres and circles, which they considered noble shapes that must be used exclusively in astronomy. This curious fixed idea caused immediate trouble, because the heavenly bodies do not follow circular courses, either in fact or in appearance. As viewed from the earth, the planets move at varying speeds, sometimes seeming to turn backwards, and wander over the sky in such a complicated way that no single set of spheres could begin to account for their behaviour.

Later Greeks tried to overcome this difficulty by adding secondary spheres attached at varying angles to the primary ones. A planet carried along on a secondary sphere would appear to follow a non-circular course that might resemble its observed motions. But two spheres per planet were not enough. Eudoxus of Cnidus (409-356 B.C.) was driven to use 27 spheres. His successors used as many as 57, but even this geometrical nightmare did not work quite correctly.

Ptolemy's persistent mistake

The most famous Greek theory is that of Claudius Ptolemy, a Greek who lived in Egypt in the second century of the Christian era and may have merely recorded the ideas of others. It has still more complications and does not adequately explain facts such as the planets' periodic changes of brightness, or to give their distances from either the earth or the sun. Critics no doubt pointed to these defects at the time, but Ptolemy lived when Greco-Roman civilization was past its creative prime. His system triumphed largely because it was the last. Transmitted by the Arabs to medieval Europe as the Almagest (which means "The Greatest" in garbled Greek), it finally acquired the force of religious dogma and might not be questioned without danger of heresy. This was unfortunate, because Ptolemy was not the best example of Greek clear thinking.

The Greeks early discarded the "commonsense" idea of a flat earth, reasoning that it must be round because of the circular shadow it casts on the moon and the way that ships seem to sink below the horizon of the sea. One inspired astronomer, Aristarchus of Samos, argued in about 275 B.C. that the sun, not the earth, is the centre of heavenly motions. He also believed that the sun was larger than the earth. We do not know today how he reached these modern-sounding conclusions; both were rejected in his time as fantastic.

Another Greek realist, Eratosthenes, estimated the size of the earth and got a surprisingly good answer. The earth's circumference came out as 250,000 stadia, a contemporary unit of length. Since the exact length of the stadium that he used is not known, his accuracy cannot be checked, but he was probably not more than 6 per cent out. Much of the best work

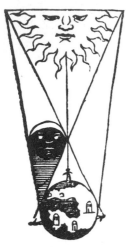

A SOLAR ECLIPSE, viewed from three positions on the earth, is accurately explained in this 16th-century Italian woodcut. To the little man at the left, the sun is obscured by the moon (*centre*) and the eclipse is total. To the man at the top of the globe, the eclipse is partial as the moon partly blocks his view. The man at the right sees no eclipse at all.

THE EARTH'S ROUNDNESS is demonstrated, as this 16th-century Italian drawing shows, by the way a departing ship seems to sink below the horizon. From the tower (*left*), the view is gradually blocked by the curvature of the earth as the ship sails away. As far back as ancient Greece, this phenomenon was correctly attributed to the roundness of the earth.

of the Greeks was not appreciated until comparatively modern times, and almost the only astronomical information that they transmitted to medieval Europe was contained in Ptolemy's elaborate, impressive but misleading Almagest. After Ptolemy came nothing of astronomical consequence for more than 1,000 years. During the long ages of ignorance that followed the decline of the Greco-Roman culture, astronomy remained dormant. Until late in the Middle Ages the few learned men of Christian Europe paid almost no attention to the sky. They did not even record the supernova, or exploding star, of A.D. 1054, which Chinese astronomers reported shone brighter than all the other stars; its remains can now be seen as the famous Crab nebula.

When European science began to stir after its long coma, the most imposing book available on astronomy and related matters remained the Almagest. In spite of its faults the work must have been a delightful revelation for scholars who had been concentrating almost exclusively on theological trivia. Its mathematics was far beyond anything known in backward Europe, and it also described Greek astronomical instruments. Medieval Christians began, timidly at first, to make and use copies of them.

So Ptolemy had a second heyday in the 15th century, but science was on a rising curve, not on a decline as in Ptolemy's own day. Together with its reverence for the past, it was beginning to show sparks of independent thought. Western European scientists took more interest in observation and experiment than the Greeks had, and depended less on unsupported ideas. While they still believed in the Ptolemaic system, 15th-century astronomers built observatories, improved Ptolemy's instruments and devised novel ones. Their observations made Ptolemy's system look worse and worse.

Criticism of Ptolemy was increasing but seldom voiced, because Western Europe had an institution unknown to the Greeks: a powerful religious bureaucracy that tried to silence anyone who differed with its official beliefs. One of its dogmas insisted that the earth must remain the large central body of the universe. This misconception is the main reason why the Ptolemaic system encountered difficulties, but anyone who pointed this out was headed for trouble.

The Great Copernican revolt

The break with the past was finally made by the Polish astronomer Nicolaus Copernicus. He prudently did not publish his great treatise, "On the Revolutions of the Heavenly Bodies", until just before he died in 1543.

The chief innovation of Copernicus was to consider the sun the centre of the solar system, just as Aristarchus had done 1,800 years before. He arranged the earth and the five planets then known in the proper order —Mercury, Venus, Earth, Mars, Jupiter, Saturn—and put them on circular orbits around the sun. The circles were a mistake, but the sun-centred system was simpler than its predecessors, and it explained better

PRIMITIVE ASTRONOMY is reflected by this drawing, discovered on the wall of an Indian cave in Arizona, and believed to have been inspired by the famous supernova, or exploding star, of 1054. The supernova did not pass between the earth and the crescent moon, but the Indians may have shown it this way because they observed that the exploding star outshone the moon. The only other record of the great cosmic event was left by Chinese astronomers. Europeans ignored it.

than they did the observation of planetary motions since Ptolemy's time.

Copernicus made no mistake in keeping his ideas out of sight. Europe was in the midst of the wars of religion, and ideological violence was commonplace. His book was fiercely attacked by conservative churchmen. On a lower intellectual level, many people of the time were outraged by the demotion of the great earth, the habitat of God-favoured men, and felt that they, personally, had been demoted with it. They reacted much as people did 400 years later when they angrily opposed Darwin's theory of evolution (some still oppose it) because it made man a flesh-and-blood relative of the lower animals. One follower of Copernicus, the great physicist Galileo, was silenced by the Church because of his belief that the earth moves around the sun. Another, Giordano Bruno, was burned at the stake by the Inquisition. Copernicus's work was put on the Church's Index of forbidden books, from which it was not removed officially until 1757.

Kepler's demotion of the earth

But in spite of conservative resistance the essential ideas of Copernicus were gradually accepted by Europe's men of learning. The earth became just one of the members of the sun's entourage. This was a revolutionary change in man's thinking about himself and the universe.

The Copernican system had serious faults, and one of the astronomers who did not accept it was Tycho Brahe, a Dane who was the best observer of the time and had the best observatory. For a lifetime he worked to overthrow Copernicus by devising a better system, and he failed chiefly because he restored the earth to its central position. When he died in 1601, he left his massive and meticulous records to his young assistant, Johannes Kepler, and trusted him to carry on the work.

Perhaps Kepler tried for a while to demolish Copernicus, but his study of Tycho's excellent records soon forced him to even more radical innovations. He not only placed the sun near the centre of the solar system but also concluded by brilliant intuition that it somehow provided the motive power for planetary movements. He did not follow up this hint of gravitation. His greatest discovery was that the planetary orbits are ellipses, a specific kind of closed oval curve, not the noble circles that the Greeks and his own contemporaries, including Copernicus, all considered necessary.

Kepler found by carefully studying Mars that its motion can be understood if its orbit is assumed to be an ellipse. The orbits of the moon, earth and the other planets proved to be ellipses too, though most of them are nearly circles. There was no need for an intricate maze of interrelated circles; just a single ellipse for each object. Kepler had achieved a great simplification, which is a kind of triumph that scientists celebrate with special rejoicing.

But Kepler had not answered the age-old question, "What holds the planets up and makes them move on their courses?" He abolished the invisible spheres of the Greeks, which after millennia had acquired a sort of spurious reality, but put nothing in their place. This would have to wait for Isaac Newton, who was not born until 1642.

When he was only 23, Newton retired to rural England to avoid a pestilence in London and began to think about the moon and the mysterious force that keeps it orbiting around the earth. It does not fly off into space, and it does not fall to earth like lesser, near-by objects. There must be some general principle behind this behaviour.

The moon as a falling body

Newton did not discover gravitation by watching an apple fall or by being hit by one, as in popular legend. Laws relating to falling objects had been studied extensively, but they had been applied only on the surface of the earth. There was no idea of gravitation as a universal force that affects all objects wherever they may be. Obviously, said the reasoning of the time, it does not apply to the heavenly bodies, since they do not fall to the earth. Newton showed his genius by applying the laws of falling bodies to the unfalling moon.

He knew from observation that an object thrown horizontally follows a curve whose flatness increases with the speed. He reasoned that perhaps the high speed of the moon, about 2,300 m.p.h., might be just enough to make it follow its known orbit in spite of its tendency to fall like other objects. Making an educated guess based on the mathematical properties of Kepler's ellipses, he assumed that as the distance from the earth increases, the force of its gravitation diminishes in proportion to the square of the distance.

Newton's first attempt to try this idea on the moon was not entirely successful, but when he got a better estimate of the earth's size it worked admirably. The moon actually moves at just the right speed for the earth's gravitation, weakened by distance, to keep it in its orbit. Newton had done an extraordinary thing, one of the greatest feats in the history of thought. He had used the familiar force that makes things fall to earth to explain why some do not.

With Newton, the framework of the solar system took its modern form, free of the mysticism of earliest times and the rational but non-existent transparent spheres of the Greeks. All its members move in response to Newton's universal force of gravitation, whose action is given in a single sentence: "Bodies attract each other with a force that varies directly as the product of their masses and inversely as the square of the distance between them". As to why Newton's law works, most scientists feel that this is a meaningless question. It happens that the universe is so made that Newton's law provides an excellent summary of the observed motions. There may be no deeper truth to it than that.

After Newton, the ancient research programme entered a new phase. The baffling central mystery had been dispelled; the mechanics of the solar system was well understood. Now its fascinating members, the earth's near neighbours in the universe, could be examined and later explored in detail.

A GREAT PLANET-WATCHER, the 16th-century Danish astronomer Tycho Brahe lived before the invention of the telescope. He made his observations with the naked eye, and recorded precise data on the motions of planets. Tycho concluded from his observations that the sun and moon revolved around the earth (*black*), while Mercury, Venus, Mars, Jupiter and Saturn—the planets known to Tycho—circled the sun. Fortunately, his records were inherited by the great astronomer Johannes Kepler, who used them to help to achieve an explanation of planetary motions similar to that held today.

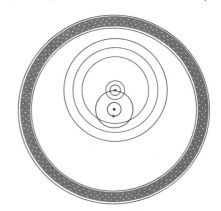

Solving the Riddle
of the Heavens

From the beginnings of history, the heavens have fascinated and challenged thoughtful men. As long ago as 3000 B.C. myths were invented to explain the origin and arrangement of the solar system as the feat of awesome gods. Later, the heavenly bodies—the sun, moon, stars and planets—were given human or animal identities and mystical qualities.

Then, some 26 centuries ago, myth and symbolism began to give way to careful observation and calculation as more painstaking investigators sought the truth about the heavens, often resorting to ingenious theories to overcome huge gaps in their knowledge. It was not until 1512, when Copernicus placed the motionless sun at the centre of the solar system, that astronomy was freed of its biggest misconception—that all other heavenly bodies revolved around a stationary earth. In the next 200 years, the workings of the solar system, including the orbital paths of the visible planets, were correctly determined. But even today the origin of the solar system remains a riddle. Despite increasingly sophisticated tools and techniques, the astronomer must use his imagination for leads—just as he has for centuries.

THE HEAVENLY PANOPLY
The heavens, observed in ancient times, seemed to be a moving spectacle above a motionless earth that occupied the centre of the universe. The moon's phases and the apparently looping path of a planet were recorded over many nights, as was the sun's "movement" through the day sky, long before men understood the relationships of the different heavenly bodies to one another.

The Sumerians' Universe

The first recorded attempt to explain the creation and composition of the heavenly bodies was made by Sumerians in the third millennium B.C.

The Sumerians, who inhabited a 300-mile-long realm between the Tigris and Euphrates rivers, gave to civilization the wheel, the plough and cuneiform writing. As befitted such innovators, they had a conception of the universe both realistic and imaginative: a sea-girt hemisphere (*below*) in which the heavenly bodies clustered in the wind above the familiar water and earth. According to Sumerian mythology, these elements were governed by the gods of creation (*right*)—giants in human shape.

THE SUMERIAN CREATION
Creating the universe, the great Enlil, Sumerian god of air, is shown wrenching apart the mountain containing both heaven and earth. According to myth, the figure in the upper portion of the mountain is Enlil's father, the god of heaven; the figure in the base is his mother, goddess of earth. The original mountain was said to have risen from the boundless eternal sea.

A TIN-ROOFED UNIVERSE
The Sumerians visualized the universe as a flat earth topped by the tin vault of heaven. Between them was the swirling atmosphere, in which the glowing sun, moon, planets and stars were controlled by the manipulations of the gods. Other early civilizations, like the Babylonian and Egyptian, modified the Sumerian concept, but accepted its supernatural premise.

A WATERY UNIVERSE

The earth, according to Thales, was a flat disc floating on the eternal water from which it had emerged. He saw water as the source of all things. He noted that it nourished life on earth and concluded that the heavens—where rain originates—must be made of evaporated water. Not only did water surround the earth but it also rimmed the heavenly vault, a vast hemisphere containing the sun, moon, all planets and stars. Thales made his deductions from simple and seemingly reasonable observations, and invoked no gods to explain his universe.

The Novel Theories of the Greeks

Greek philosophers subjected earlier myths concerning the universe to painstaking inquiry. Because they sought a "first principle" as a basic cause of all phenomena, the Greeks came up with some imaginative, if inaccurate, explanations of the universe. In the sixth century B.C. the philosopher Thales reasoned that water must be the raw material from which the universe was produced (*above*). Anaximander, a friend of Thales, held that the universe began with a sphere of fire enclosing a cold, moist mass, from which it was separated by a layer of mist. Eventually, the cold mass became the earth, the fire became the light of the heavenly bodies, and the mist the surrounding atmosphere (*right*).

In the fifth century B.C., Philolaos adopted a radically different approach. Believing the number 10 to signify perfection, he presupposed a universe of 10 heavenly bodies. Since only nine—five planets, the sun, the moon, the earth and the sphere of the stars—were visible, a tenth, the counter-earth, was invented. Arbitrary as this system was, it was the first to picture the earth as a revolving sphere like other planets (*opposite*).

ANAXIMANDER'S FIERY RINGS

At the centre of Anaximander's universe, which sprang not from any single element but from what he called a "germ" of fused opposites, was a free-floating earth shaped like a drum. Surrounding it were fiery rings enclosed in mist through which the heavenly bodies rolled, appearing through openings in the mist. Anaximander placed the "cooler" stars nearest the earth. Beyond the moon and sun the fiercest fires burned—a fiery sphere about the universe.

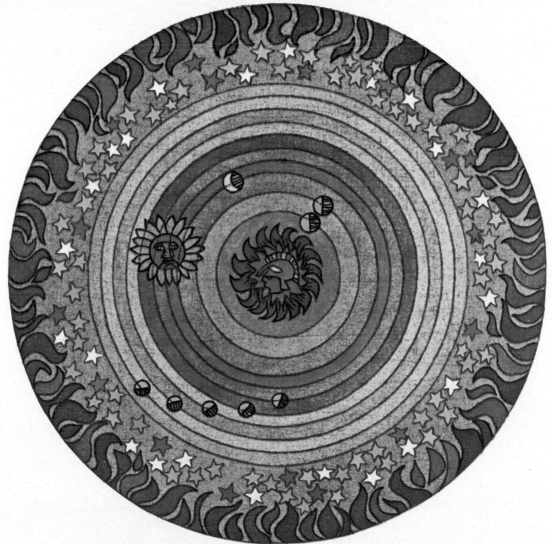

PHILOLAOS'S CIRCLING SPHERES

In the revolutionary design of Philolaos, the earth appears as a sphere and no longer occupies the centre of the universe. Instead, a "central fire" burns at the core and illuminates the sun. Between this fire and the earth, a pro-tective counter-earth revolves, invisible from the hemisphere where all the earth's population was thought to live. The heavenly bodies, including the five other known planets, revolve on circular paths within an envelope of fire.

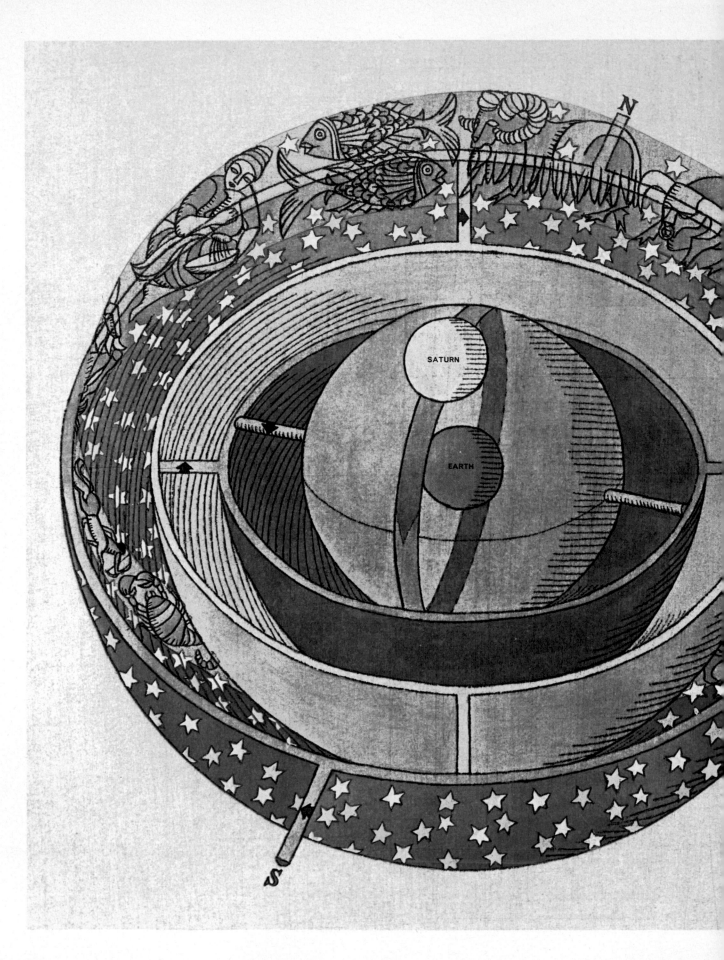

A System of Circles and Spheres

Early Greek philosophers pondered the universe with little more than their logic and eyesight to help them. But later Greeks applied maturing mathematical skills to the problem of heavenly movements. As early as the fourth century B.C., Eudoxus sought a formula to explain what appeared to be looping planetary paths (*below*). Believing that planets orbited the earth in perfect circles, Eudoxus drew 27 concentric spheres around the earth. Each sphere, or any body within it, was calculated to rotate on a different axis. Eudoxus could approximate the motions of any heavenly body by combining the movements of these spheres (*left*).

But Eudoxus's clever theory left unexplained why planets dimmed and grew bright, indicating variations in their distance from the earth. In the second century A.D. the astronomer-cartographer Ptolemy devised a system in which planets revolved in small circles while orbiting the earth (*right*). Thus, Ptolemy "proved" that a planet might be close to the earth at one sighting and distant at another, while its principal motion remained a circle around the earth.

CIRCLES IN THE SKY
Ptolemy devised the above scheme to explain Saturn's apparent looping path and changing brightness as observed from the earth. He assumed that Saturn travelled in a small yearly orbit which itself revolved in a large circle around a slightly off-centre earth once every 30 years. The 8 positions shown above indicate where Saturn happens to be on its small orbit at selected intervals of its 30-year journey. The arcs indicate not the planet's motion but the displacement from its faintest positions—those farthest from the earth. For example, Saturn appears brightest when nearest the earth (*bottom position*) and faintest when farthest from it (*top position*).

LOOPING THE LOOP
Saturn's looping path (*above*), traced over a three-year period as it crosses the constellations of Pisces and part of Aries—one-ninth of the heavenly zodiac—was explained by Eudoxus by means of the chart on the left. Not only did he have Saturn (*blue*) describing a circular orbit around a central earth, but the inner sphere in which it orbited was itself revolving on an axis attached to a revolving outer sphere. Four such spheres were needed to explain Saturn's twists as seen from the earth, and 27 spheres supposedly produced the motions of the whole solar system. The outermost sphere, which rotated around the earth daily, contained the stars on which are superimposed the symbolic figures of the zodiac.

23

The Sun
Stops Moving

"Although the idea seemed absurd," wrote the famous 16th-century Polish astronomer Nicolaus Copernicus, "I began to think of a motion of the earth." Once it was assumed that the earth itself rotated each day—rather than having all the other heavenly bodies rush around the earth every 24 hours—the motions of the planets, said Copernicus, became more comprehensible.

Having challenged the established notion of a fixed earth, Copernicus ventured further. In 1512 he put the sun, instead of the earth, at the centre of the solar system (*right*). However, he still believed that the planets orbited in perfect circles.

It was not until 1609 that the German astronomer Johannes Kepler described planetary paths correctly for the first time. Agreeing with Copernicus that the planets were sun-centred, Kepler began to question the notion of circular orbits. His calculations, based on voluminous and precise observations, indicated elliptical orbits instead. Proceeding on this assumption, Kepler then proved that the speed of a planet depends on its distance from the sun (*opposite, top*). This finding, broadened by Newton into his gravitation law, ended, once and for all, the age-old speculations on the motions of the solar system.

CIRCLING THE SUN
At the centre of Copernicus's planetary system (*right*) is the sun, "sitting on the royal throne". The earth together with its satellite, the moon, was but one of six known planets that circled the sun. Copernicus placed the planets in their proper sequence for the first time—Mercury and Venus between the sun and the earth; Mars, Jupiter and Saturn between earth and stars.

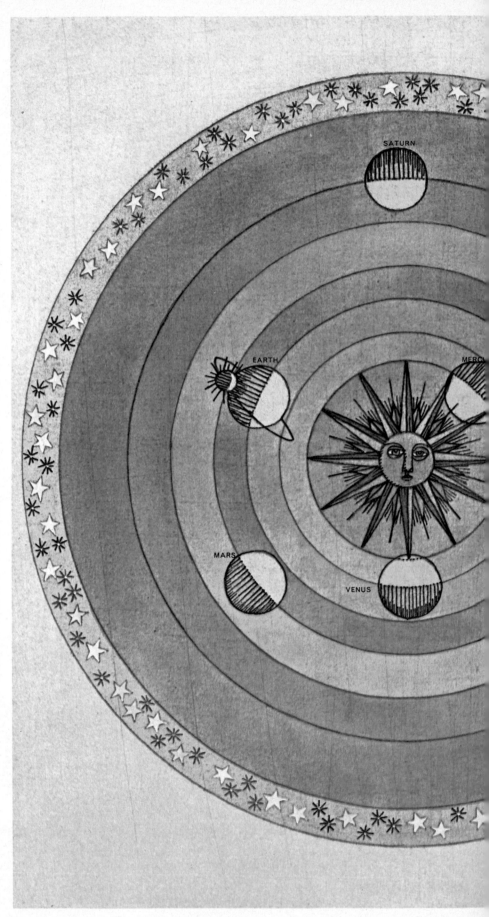

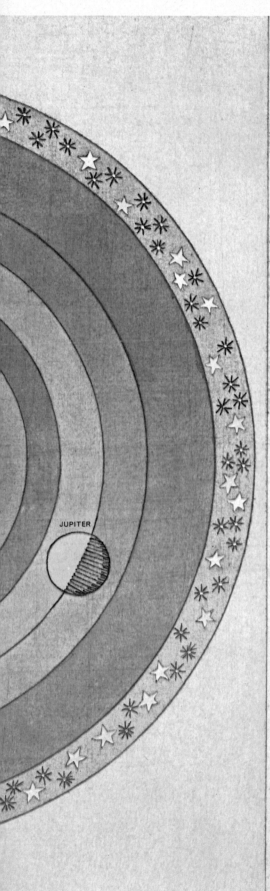

CHANGING SPEEDS IN ORBIT
Orbiting in its elliptical course, Mars speeds up when near the sun (perihelion) and slows down farther away (aphelion), taking the same time to cover the two different distances shown. Kepler proved that all planets described such elliptical orbits.

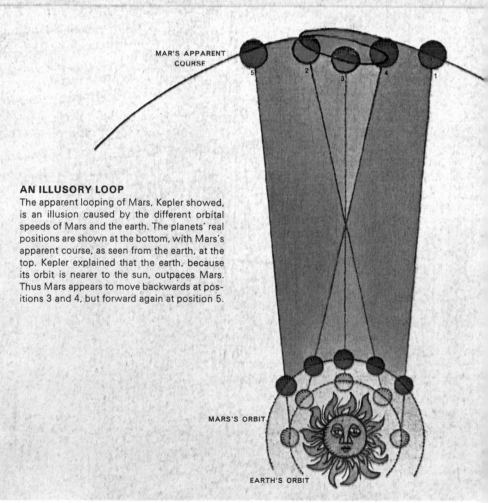

AN ILLUSORY LOOP
The apparent looping of Mars, Kepler showed, is an illusion caused by the different orbital speeds of Mars and the earth. The planets' real positions are shown at the bottom, with Mars's apparent course, as seen from the earth, at the top. Kepler explained that the earth, because its orbit is nearer to the sun, outpaces Mars. Thus Mars appears to move backwards at positions 3 and 4, but forward again at position 5.

Planets from a Cloud of Gas

Even though Copernicus and Kepler correctly arranged the solar system, the mystery of its beginnings still defies solution. Curiously, it was not an astronomer but the great German philosopher Immanuel Kant who first propounded in 1755 the most enduring and renowned of all scientific theories seeking to explain the origin of the solar system—the nebular hypothesis.

According to Kant, the solar system was developed from an enormous cloud, or nebula, of gas. Kant thought of this cloud as having been originally cool and motionless. The particles in it were pulled together by their gravitational attraction for one another, and somehow began rotating in a common direction. As this nebula became more compressed, Kant said, it grew hotter and hotter, until it glowed into a giant primitive sun. As the sun contracted, Kant suggested, its rate of spin steadily increased until it finally cast off the gaseous rings from which the planets were formed, one at a time.

In 1796 the French scientist Pierre Simon, Marquis de Laplace, independently advanced an hypothesis similar to Kant's. The main difference was that Laplace thought of the gaseous nebula as heated and rotating from the very start. A better mathematician than Kant, he knew that the mere act of condensation could never have started such a nebula rotating. Although some of the details in the Kant Laplace nebular hypothesis have been modified over the years, its principle is still accepted today.

1

3

2

4

1 A GASEOUS NEBULA

A vast, hot, slowly rotating nebula of gas forms the first stage in Laplace's hypothesis of how the solar system began. As it rotated, the outer regions of the nebula began to cool. Laplace thought the original size of this primeval gaseous globe must have been larger than the dimensions of the solar system he knew: i.e., to the orbit of Uranus. Beyond lay the stars.

2 THE EJECTED RINGS

In the second stage the rotating mass contracted, meanwhile spinning with increasing velocity. Just as mud is thrown off the rim of a swiftly spinning car wheel, gaseous rings were ejected from the main body. In this drawing, a newly separated ring is shown just outside the whirling core. Beyond it, a previously ejected ring is beginning to break up into clouds of gas.

3 THE FORMING PLANETS

The solar system begins to take shape as the clouds of gas condense and recombine. This condensation process has already produced the round shape of a planet, and another gas ring is shown gathering into whorls which, as they cool, will also form a planet. The core of the shrinking nebula, still ejecting its rings of matter, is beginning to resemble the familiar sun.

4 A SYSTEM IN SPACE

A stable sun, throwing off no more rings, is surrounded by fully formed embryonic planets in the concluding stage of the Kant-Laplace hypothesis. The planets shown closest to the sun—Mercury, Venus and the earth—are the last to condense. The planets are already circling the sun in orbits corresponding to their former rings, in the same direction as the sun's rotation.

A Tide of Gas
Torn from the Sun

Not until the 20th century did a theory on the origin of the solar system seriously challenge the Kant-Laplace nebular hypothesis (*pages 26-27*). Proposed by Sir James Jeans in 1901, the tidal theory avoided the unanswered problem of how the nebula had begun to spin and appeared to explain (*right*) the planet sizes.

Jeans envisioned the birth of the solar system as a rare event which occurred when the sun was almost side-swiped by a star (*below, left*). The result of this near-miss was a tidal effect in which a mass of hot solar matter was torn off—the material from which the planets were made.

Jeans's theory seemed sound until, in the 1930's, two flaws were found. Mathematical studies showed that no grazing star could have started the tide moving fast enough to match the revolutionary momentum of the planets. Even if that were possible, the hot solar matter would not have condensed into planets, but probably would have expanded and dispersed.

A SIDE-SWIPED SUN
In Jeans's hypothesis, a passing star nearly grazes the sun, generating an immense tide in the solar surface. According to Jeans, this surge rose in a huge mountain as the star approached and then "darted out as a long tongue of gas". As the star continued into space, a long filament of solar matter remained, detached from the sun but still within its gravitational field.

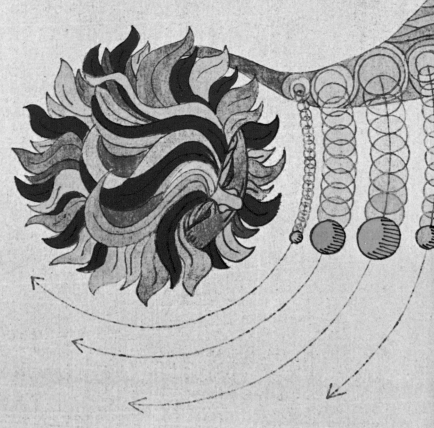

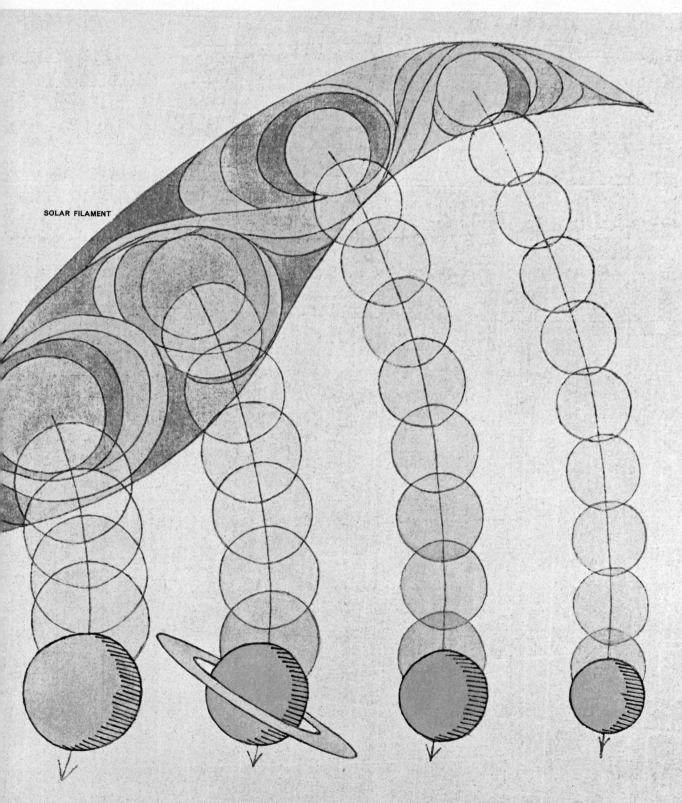

SOLAR FILAMENT

THE PLANET-BEARING FILAMENT

The 8 planets known in Jeans's day are shown being formed from the long solar filament extending into space, their sizes determined by the varying thickness of the tide. The planets at either end, Mercury and Neptune, are comparatively small, while those forming out of the centre, Jupiter and Saturn, are large. Jeans's theory accounted for the sizes of the planets, which are drawn approximately to scale above. A ninth and more distant planet, Pluto, was not discovered until 1930.

29

An Old Hypothesis Revised

Modern research has added new validity to the old hypothesis that a solar nebula gave birth to the planets. Though the sun now rotates about once every 27 days, recent calculations indicate that the primitive sun must have spun much faster to throw off the material that became planets. But what could have slowed it down?

A group of astronomers, including Britain's Fred Hoyle and Sweden's Hannes Alfvén, provided an answer in the 1950's—that the rotational momentum of the sun was transferred by magnetic lines of force to a disc of gaseous material the sun left behind (*below*). So efficiently was this done that today the sun accounts for only

MAGNETIC LINES OF FORCE

2 per cent of the momentum of rotation and revolution of bodies in the solar system; planets have the rest.

Because most stars—distant suns —are rotating slowly like our sun, it is possible that they too have been slowed by a similar process of planet formation. If so, the universe may be dotted with worlds like our own.

SLOWING DOWN THE SUN

The still-forming, rapidly rotating sun spins with its disc of gas in this conception of the Hoyle-Alfvén hypothesis. Magnetic lines of force emerge from the sun, enter the disc and convey the sun's spin to it. As long as the sun turns faster than the disc, these lines of force will twist backwards until, like springs, they will slow down the sun while forcing the disc outwards. Thus, most of the sun's rotational momentum passes to the disc—and the planets.

2

The Most
Familiar
Planet

The earth from 35,000 feet, this view of the Carolinas shows the atmosphere's bluish tint.

A CONVENIENT STARTING POINT for investigating the planets is the earth, the planet that can be studied with the greatest ease. Although it is quite feasible to land men and instruments on the moon and some of the planets and to study them with instruments on close-flying space craft, the information gained in this way is fragmentary. It might be totally baffling without the knowledge we have of other celestial bodies that provides a frame of reference to evaluate new findings.

An effective strategy for interpreting data about distant planets is to assume that the planets are fundamentally similar to the earth, differing chiefly in ways that can be accounted for by planetary evolution. Astronomers believe that the earth was formed at the same time as the other planets and out of similar materials. The same star—the sun— bombarded them all with the same kinds of radiation for about 4,500 million years, and the same laws of physics and chemistry governed the development of all. They are bound to have features in common, and when these are identified, whole blocks of information amassed about the earth can be transferred, with caution, to other planets.

So a key to the planets is knowledge of the earth, including its earliest history. Without this guiding example the shreds of knowledge that astronomers gather so painfully with their long-distance instruments would be very much more difficult to interpret correctly.

Until recently no human eye, or even a camera lens, had seen the entire earth as a planet, but astronomers had long before predicted fairly accurately what it would look like from far off in space. It would be bluish, they said, instead of yellowish like Venus or reddish like Mars. The globe would be wrapped in a light-blue haze caused by the preferential scattering of the blue component of sunlight by the atmosphere. This same scattering also makes the sky look blue from the surface of our own planet.

When space craft carrying cameras got far enough from the earth they proved these predictions correct. The earth seen from a distance is bluish. It is not as bright as Venus because of its lower reflectivity and greater distance from the sun, and its surface markings are not as distinct as those of Mars because of its thicker atmosphere and brilliant white clouds. Through the haze and gaps in covering clouds the continents show dimly in soft pastel colours, often without sharp boundaries.

From the distance of Venus at its nearest approach (26 million miles) a large telescope could, with difficulty, detect seasonal changes on the earth —snowfalls, cloudless seasons, the growth of vegetation—but they would not be as conspicuous as the seasonal changes on Mars. No works of man would be visible. The observers would get almost no hint of the enormous complexity and variety, both natural and artificial, that the earth's inhabitants know to exist on and near its surface.

Most of the earth's characteristics that concern man are found in three outside layers that are hardly more than surface films when compared to the earth as a whole. Practically all the atmosphere lies below 100 miles, and the solid rocky crust of the earth is never more than 40 miles thick, usually much thinner. Between them over most of the surface lies the ocean, which averages less than two miles deep. If the earth were the size of an apple, its crust and atmosphere added together would be about as thick as the apple's skin.

Inside this thin skin lies the bulk of the earth, a hot, not quite solid sphere nearly 8,000 miles in diameter. Its interior has not been seen or sampled, and it has little direct effect on the surface where man lives. But the central mass created the surface layers, which grew on it during its long life like the tarnish that accumulates on an old bronze statue.

Vibrations of the elastic earth

Knowledge of the earth's interior, and by inference its past history, comes mostly from seismology, the science of interpreting earthquake waves. Earthquakes are frequent in the modern earth, most of them caused by movements of the crust that make sudden breaks along "faults", or lines of weakness. When the break occurs, the slightly elastic rock shakes like a broken spring and a long series of vibrations spreads away from the point of breakage. If the vibrations are strong enough they can be detected on the far side of the earth with seismographs, which are instruments consisting essentially of suspended weights whose inertia keeps them motionless while the earth vibrates beneath them. The relative motion between the weight and the ground is amplified by a delicate apparatus and recorded as a zigzag line on a band of paper. By studying this record, seismologists can use the waves as messengers to report what kind of material they have encountered during their journeys through the earth.

The waves that plunge deep through the earth are of different kinds. P waves (primary waves) are pressure waves like sound waves in air; they vibrate longitudinally in the direction of their travel. S waves (secondary waves) are like the waves that move along a rope fixed at one end and shaken at the other. Their vibration is across the direction of their travel. Both are made to curve by changes in the physical nature of the material through which they pass, and both are partially reflected by boundaries between different materials. The S waves do not pass through liquids, only through solids, so they serve as a way to find out whether any part of the earth's interior is truly liquid.

Interpretation of seismograms (the records of seismographs) is extremely complicated and gives rise to endless arguments about details, but a general knowledge of the earth's interior, agreed to by nearly all experts, has been extracted from their wiggly lines. The most important single fact is that the earth has a heavy liquid core. It is known to be liquid because the S waves refuse to pass through it. Its density, reported by the P waves, which do pass through it, is right for molten iron under high compression and perhaps alloyed with small amounts of other materials. Any theory about the earth's early history must explain the core, which is 4,300 miles in diameter, bigger than Mars.

A generation ago it was commonly taught that the earth and the planets were torn out of the sun by a star that happened to pass near by.

A JAR TO LOCATE EARTHQUAKES, this Chinese seismograph of the second century A.D. had a pendulum arranged to swing away from the shock wave's source (*opposite page*) In this diagram, an earthquake has caused the pendulum to swing to the left, forcing open the mouth of one of eight bronze dragon's heads mounted around the jar (only two show in this cross-sectional view). The dragon then drops a ball into the mouth of a bronzed toad sitting below. To determine from which direction the shock wave came, an observer looked to see which one of the eight toads had a ball in its mouth. This ancient instrument was probably used only to record earthquakes. Modern seismographs are so sensitive to a variety of waves (*opposite*) that they have become valuable tools for obtaining information on the composition of the earth's inner layers.

This "catastrophic" theory is now out of favour. Most astronomers and geophysicists, both of whom claim the birth of the solar system as part of their jurisdiction, believe that planet formation is a normal process that can happen near any young growing star.

About 5,000 million years ago (says the most favoured current theory) a large cloud of dust and gas (mostly hydrogen) floating in space began to concentrate by mutual gravitational attraction somewhere near the centre, to form the nucleus of the star that is now called the sun. This body's increase in size made its gravitation stronger and pulled more gas and dust towards it. How long this process took is not known accurately, but eventually the new-formed star got big enough to heat its centre to many million degrees and to start thermonuclear reactions somewhat like those that take place in a hydrogen bomb. Nuclear energy released by turning hydrogen into helium made the interior of the new-formed sun hot, the nuclear reactions continued, and it shone stably as a star. It has been shining ever since.

Swirling newborn planets

Astronomers are not sure how the sun's planets managed to condense out of the remnants of the original cloud. The nuclei were small at first and their gravitation was too weak to make objects falling on them hit them very hard. As their mass increased, however, their gravitation grew stronger, and the smaller bodies that they collected hit them with meteor speed, releasing large amounts of impact energy. The bombardment may have heated the young planets to some extent. But for perhaps 500 million years their interior stayed solid and well under 1,000°C., which is cool by geophysical standards. The next stage of development is not known with any confidence for any planet except the earth, though other planets probably evolved in a related manner.

A clue to the earth's condition in its early youth is provided by certain kinds of meteorites, which are believed to be left-over examples of the small bodies that clustered together to form the planets. Since they contain mostly metallic iron and silicate rock, the earth is thought of as having been formed as a coolish globe of iron and silicates, well mixed together.

Along with these main ingredients were small amounts of other elements, some of them radioactive. The most important were uranium, thorium and potassium, which are present today, but there must also have been short-lived radioactive elements that have now decayed to more common non-radioactive elements. As millions of years passed, energy released by radioactive decay gradually heated the earth until some of its constituents melted. The iron melted before most of the silicates, and since it was heavier it tended to sink towards the centre, forcing up the silicates that it found there. The earth need not have been largely molten for iron to have migrated to the interior.

At the height of this turnover, the surface must have been a spectacular place. Reflecting the turmoil below as the iron descended, the sur-

S WAVE

P WAVE

TWO KINDS OF SEISMIC WAVES from earthquakes, laterally vibrating S waves and compressional P waves (*above*), are used by seismologists to study the structure of the earth's inner layers. Some P waves are known to pass through liquids, while S waves merely bounce off them. Thus, when the scientists noted that P waves penetrated the earth's outer core while the S waves did not (*below*), they concluded the outer core was liquid. Scientists will use this method to study the interior of other planets, and seismological instruments have "soft-landed" on the moon.

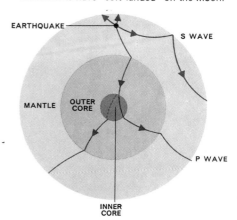

EARTHQUAKE

S WAVE

MANTLE OUTER CORE

P WAVE

INNER CORE

face heaved and bubbled gigantically, with volcanoes exploding through it and lava flowing over large parts of it. At last most of the iron reached the centre, where it accumulated as the core. The earth quietened down and formed a thin but fairly stable crust of solid rock.

The earth's interior fires

The earth's metal core is now fairly hot, probably around 3,900°C. Most of it is fluid, but there is evidence that the highly compressed centre is solid. The fluid portion is believed to be in circulation, probably caused by heat-induced currents and by the effect of the earth's rotation. This motion is the cause of the earth's magnetic field that makes compass needles point north and south. The details are far from clear, but geophysicists consider magnetism an important clue to a planet's inner character. If a planet possesses a magnetic field, it probably has something like a fluid metallic core. If it lacks a magnetic field, it probably has no core, or a solid, motionless one.

Outside the core is the earth's mantle, which extends almost to the surface and is something between solid and liquid. Like that entertaining substance, Silly Putty, it reacts to sudden motions, such as earthquake waves, like a solid, but flows like a liquid in response to large, long-continued pressures. The mantle is 1,800 miles thick and is made of heavy silicate rock much like the basalt brought to the surface today by volcanic eruptions. Most of the earth's uranium, thorium and potassium are in the outer crust, but the mantle contains some of these radioactive elements, and the heat that they continue to give off contributes to making the earth an active, moderately unstable body.

Generation of heat in any mass of material is apt to cause movement. The young earth was comparatively cool on the outside because of loss of heat to space. Then, as its interior grew hot through radioactivity, the deep-down material expanded, became lighter and tended to rise towards the surface in convection currents, like hot air rising over a stove. Some geophysicists think a single vertical current started flowing before the core had a chance to form, and passed right through the earth, rising to the surface on one side and sinking down on the other. It forced horizontal currents to flow on the surface itself, and these carried a "scum" of light surface rock towards the place where the vertical current sank down. The scum accumulated there as a great raft of light rock that floated above the general level of the surface. Geophysicists call this raft the "ur-continent" (original continent), and many of them believe that it broke up later into the nuclei of the present continents.

There is much dispute about this, however. All geophysicists now agree that the continents are made of comparatively light rock, mostly granite, and that they float like icebergs in the slightly yielding mantle, but some insist they are of alien origin. Back in its youth, this hypothesis says, the earth was made entirely of heavy rock like the mantle. Then one or more smaller bodies made of lighter rock plunged into it, and their material spread out on the surface to form the high-standing

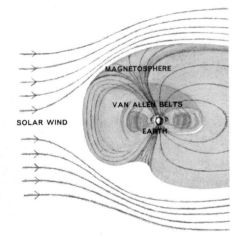

THE VAN ALLEN BELTS, two bands of charged particles trapped by the earth's magnetic field, were discovered in 1959 by physicist James Van Allen while analysing radiation data from early Explorer and Pioneer rockets. Explorer XII later indicated that the belts were high-intensity zones of a larger band of radiation called the magnetosphere, extending to about 40,000 miles out from the earth. A similar band of charged particles is known to encircle Jupiter.

continents. A body 1,400 miles in diameter would provide enough material for all the continents, while a modern asteroid the size of Ceres (diameter 440 miles) would supply enough for Australia or Antarctica.

There are several objections to this idea. A more widely favoured view holds that the continents were created by currents that flowed for thousands of millions of years in the mantle, stopping intermittently and starting again. After the core had formed, it blocked any single current that may have been flowing through the earth's centre. In place of the single current were several convective cells, or streams of slowly rising and sinking material. One of the currents may have risen under the ur-continent, making it split and moving the fragments apart like pieces of a broken ice floe. This is one explanation of continental drift, a theory originally based on the similarity of the opposite shores of the Atlantic. If North and South America were moved towards Europe-Africa, they would fit together nicely with a little pushing, and the old coal-bearing mountains of North America would neatly join the coal districts of Europe.

Continents that float

The startling idea that the great continents have drifted like logs in a pond was scoffed at for many years, but recently it has come to be generally accepted. It is known that when certain kinds of rock are formed, either by settling sediment or cooling lava, magnetic particles in them behave like compass needles, lining up with the earth's magnetic field, which for fundamental reasons tends to point north and south. This happened in ancient rocks too, and if they had stayed in the same position since their formation, their magnetism would still point north and south. In some cases it does, but many ancient rocks have been found with fossil magnetism pointing in other directions, indicating that they have shifted position and supporting the theory that the continents have drifted widely. Final proof came when extensive mapping of the sea floor, begun by the U.S. Navy after World War II, revealed a mighty earth-girding mountain range, cleft along its crest by a rift that emits heat and is punctuated by volcanic areas. Scientists now agree that convection currents from the mantle below force up partly molten rock, which oozes through this open seam in the form of basalt lava and pushes the earth's crust slowly to both sides. Not only are the continents thus adrift, but their movement actually causes some of them to split up.

Mexico's peninsula of Lower California and the part of the U.S. State of California that includes Los Angeles are moving towards the Aleutian Islands at the rate of two inches per year, breaking away from North America along the line of the famous San Andreas Fault that passes through San Francisco. Another movement is separating Africa from Asia. The Red Sea and the deep rift lakes of East Africa may grow in a few hundred million years into an ocean as wide as the Atlantic.

Whether other planets have similar motions in their interiors and crusts is unknown. But for man the earth's surface, thinly wrapped in water and air, is the most important zone of the planet. So once the major features of the crust have been accounted for, the next step is to trace the history of the oceans and atmosphere, which together hold the secrets of the origin of life.

Astronomers who study the sun and stars know that they are made almost entirely of hydrogen and helium. These light gases are extremely scarce on the earth, which is made predominantly of heavy materials. Something must have happened to separate the cosmically rare heavy elements from the hydrogen and helium that made up most of the cloud out of which the sun and its planets were formed. The most successful theories hold that the sun drove the light gases away.

It is a basic physical principle that when gases are mixed together at any uniform temperature, most of their atoms (or molecules) are moving rapidly, and the higher the temperature the faster their average speed. The light ones also move faster than heavier ones. Hydrogen, the lightest, moves fastest of all, followed by helium, the second lightest. When the earth was being formed, any hydrogen or helium atoms near it were made to move so fast by solar radiation that they escaped from the earth's gravitation just as if they were rockets exceeding the modern earth's escape velocity. Heavier gases went with them, perhaps during a brief period in the sun's youth when it was much more luminous than it is now.

An earth devoid of atmosphere

Their departure left the earth almost bare of gases, so its present atmosphere must have come out of the interior, accumulating slowly as the ages passed. This idea is easier to accept when it is remembered that the atmosphere, which seems large to dwellers on the earth's surface, is less than one-millionth of the planet's total mass. The oceans are about one four-thousandth of the total, and so a modest amount of outgassing—escape of volatile constituents from the interior—can easily account for both of them many times over.

The outgassing still continues, though probably not as strongly as before. Besides the gases that roar so conspicuously out of volcanoes, a probably larger contribution comes from volatile matter that escapes from steam vents or seeps quietly through the floor of the ocean. It has been calculated that modern hot springs contribute enough "juvenile" water (water that has never been to the surface before) to replace the entire ocean in about 3,000 million years.

It is very likely that the young earth's first outgassed atmosphere was very different from its present one. Still reflecting the cosmic abundance of the elements, it was composed predominantly of hydrogen and hydrogen-rich gases. In such a "reducing" atmosphere no free oxygen can form. Besides inert nitrogen, it contained methane, the principal component of natural gas, ammonia, water vapour and perhaps a small amount of carbon dioxide.

The water vapour in it was vulnerable to destruction by ultra-violet light coming from the sun. At present these powerful rays are absorbed

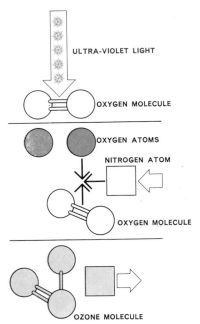

THE FORMATION OF OZONE from molecules of oxygen in the upper atmosphere (*shown above*) is part of a cyclic series of chemical reactions that prevents lethal rays of ultra-violet light from reaching the earth. The process starts when ultra-violet light (*arrow*), streaming down from the sun, hits an oxygen molecule and breaks its atoms apart. The impact adds momentum to the unhitched oxygen atoms and one of them undergoes a three-way collision (*middle*) with another oxygen molecule and a molecule such as nitrogen (*square*). The result is a molecule of ozone. Eventually the ozone will absorb an ultra-violet ray and break down into oxygen to start the cycle again. It is this last process that shields life on earth from the most lethal rays.

by oxygen at high altitudes where there is little or no water, but in the early years, when oxygen was lacking, the ultra-violet light could reach water molecules and split them into hydrogen and oxygen. Most of the hydrogen quickly escaped into space while the oxygen reacted with methane or ammonia, forming principally carbon dioxide, nitrogen and water, or was absorbed by oxygen-hungry materials in the earth's crust.

This process of splitting water molecules, which is called photodissociation, may have been slow, but it gradually removed by oxidation part of the methane and other reducing gases in the atmosphere. Specialists in the early history of the earth do not agree as to whether it yielded any permanent free oxygen, but it certainly made it easier for oxygen to accumulate by eliminating some of the gases which react with oxygen. And about 4,000 million years ago, perhaps earlier, a much more remarkable process was beginning: the first feeble start of life, which would eventually control the composition of the atmosphere.

It is not easy to imagine the earth 4,000 million years ago. Perhaps it had oceans covering much of its surface, perhaps only separate seas in low places. There was no life, not even bacteria. In that strange unbreathable atmosphere, the sky must have been blue; presumably it had clouds, and rain fell from them, for traces of water erosion are found in rocks formed considerably earlier.

The sunlight reaching the surface then contained ultra-violet rays that would kill most modern creatures, but this same ultra-violet also had the apparently paradoxical effect of helping the start of life. When its powerful ultra-violet rays broke up simple molecules in the atmosphere, some of the fragments united to form organic compounds such as aldehydes and cyanides. These, being heavier than most atmospheric constituents, sank to the surface or were washed down by rain.

The ancient soupy oceans

Gradually the new compounds accumulated in the growing oceans. As millions of years passed and these compounds interacted, the ocean water became a solution of organic matter whose molecules joined together under the stimulus of ultra-violet light, growing larger and more complicated. Some of them were compounds that play key parts in the chemistry of life on the earth today. They could not possibly survive in the modern ocean, where they would be snapped up as food by microorganisms, but in the ancient ocean there was nothing alive to eat them so they survived and accumulated. The ocean may have grown as rich in organic material as *consommé*.

This is not mere guesswork or scientific romancing. The first steps of the process can be duplicated in the laboratory by putting methane, ammonia, water and hydrogen in a sealed glass container to simulate the ancient atmosphere, and passing electric sparks through them to play the part of the energy that was added by ultra-violet light or lightning. The product is a rich organic mixture including amino acids, the building blocks of the proteins. More elaborate experiments, some of

△ ADENINE

○ SUGAR

□ PHOSPHATE

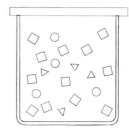

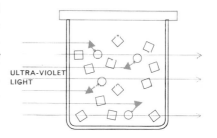

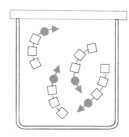

THE FUEL OF EARTHLY LIFE, adenosine triphosphate (ATP), may have been created from simple substances floating in a primeval sea. These drawings indicate how ancient ultra-violet radiation acting on three such substances—adenine, sugar and phosphate—could cause them to unite in energy-charged molecules of ATP (*bottom*). Ultra-violet activity on other planets may have formed similar organic molecules, and perhaps even life itself.

which used ultra-violet light, have proved that many other substances of biological importance can be synthesized out of simple compounds by the natural action of physical and chemical laws in primitive planetary environments. The long list includes ATP (adenosine triphosphate), which stores energy in vital life processes, and the nucleotides, the building blocks of nucleic acids, the basic hereditary materials.

Oceans of evolving creatures

If such feats of creation are possible in the laboratory, it is no strain on credulity to believe that an ocean of organic solution illuminated by ultra-violet for a thousand million years might produce a great variety of molecules, including very complex ones that would have some of the attributes of living organisms, gathering material from their surroundings, using it for growth and storing sufficient information to make accurate replicas of themselves. If such molecules have, in addition, the ability to evolve and become more efficient, they can be considered truly alive.

This is what is believed to have happened about 4,000 million years ago. The organisms that came into existence then were certainly very much simpler than the humblest modern bacteria or viruses, perhaps even simpler than the large molecules of nucleic acid that control the reproduction of all modern living things. These organisms probably lived sluggishly, taking a long time to multiply. For a while there may have been several or many kinds with different chemistry. If the earth had separate seas with no connections between them for long periods, which is quite possible, each sea may have developed its own types of life.

But true Darwinian evolution was at work at the molecular level. By accidental changes (mutation), a few of the organisms became more efficient and passed their advantages to their descendants. They multiplied faster, and starved their weaker rivals by competition for food in the soupy water. At last came a turning point when a single organism blessed by a favourable evolutionary change became so much more efficient than the others that its swarming progeny spread through the waters of the primitive earth, exterminating all competitors. There is little doubt that this great event actually happened. The proof is that every organism alive on earth today, from bacterium to man, has the same complicated basic chemistry. So all must be descendants of that single triumphant, submicroscopic speck that conquered the oceans so long ago.

For a long time, perhaps several hundred million years, the primitive organisms remained small, inefficient and not nearly so numerous as the creatures that swarm in the modern ocean. Their only food was the ocean's sparse and probably dwindling supply of organic material, created by ultra-violet light. But they were evolving and improving. Eventually some of them developed the ability to absorb ordinary visible light and use its energy to make food materials out of water and carbon dioxide.

This process, photosynthesis, gave great new impetus to life on earth. No longer need life depend on a chance trickle of food. The new photosynthetic organisms—plants—could make their own food, limited only by the bounty of readily available sunlight. Animals promptly evolved to eat the plants and multiply along with them.

Green-plant photosynthesis meant the end of the earth's early atmosphere. When the newly evolved plants used carbon dioxide and water to make sugars and other foods, the reaction dissociated the water to release large quantities of free oxygen. The process was probably slow at first, starting in shallow, sunlit pools where photosynthesis was especially active. Later the oxygen spread throughout the oceans and air. Eventually it eliminated almost all methane, ammonia and other reducing compounds, and then began to accumulate in the atmosphere.

The great life cycle

The earth's modern atmosphere has about 20 per cent oxygen, and there is no doubt about where it came from. The photosynthesis of existing plants on land and in the oceans is vigorous enough to supply all of it in 2,000 years, a mere tick of the clock on the geologic time scale. Animals large and small eat the plants, take in oxygen by breathing, and exhale carbon dioxide, which is reabsorbed by the plants, thus completing the carbon cycle that is the mainspring of life. At present the plants are far ahead. The atmosphere and the ocean contain only a trace of carbon dioxide. The plants absorb it as fast as the animals that have eaten their fellow plants put it back in circulation.

The modern atmosphere is dominated by the plants, and its richness in oxygen makes it unique among the planets. Apparently the earthly type of photosynthesis is not in operation anywhere else in the solar system. This does not mean in itself that life does not exist on other planets. If the earth's atmosphere had been examined before photosynthesis won its victory thousands of millions of years ago, it would have shown no more than a trace of free oxygen, but nevertheless life was in full development in the oceans. Other planets may have kinds of life that do not release oxygen.

Though astronomers know they will not find earth-like conditions anywhere, they minutely study the earth's atmosphere as a key to the characteristics of other atmospheres which will have controlling effects on the surfaces and climates of their planets. But understanding the earth's atmosphere is not easy. It looks simple enough when examined from the ground with uninstructed eyes, but actually it is a many-layered thing, in constant complicated motion.

In a sense the ocean is part of the atmosphere, since it is made of easily volatile material and owes its liquid state to a delicate balance of temperature. It can also be considered part of the earth's crust because part of it is frozen solid in glaciers and ice caps, which were bigger during at least two major periods of geologic history.

They may get bigger again or even disappear, and the size of oceans may fluctuate. If the temperature of the earth's surface should rise by only a couple of degrees, part of the liquid water would join the atmosphere as water vapour. A sufficient increase would dry it up entirely, giv-

A CLUE TO PLANETARY LIFE may be offered by these fossils, discovered in ancient rock by Harvard scientists. The primitive fossil above, the oldest yet found, dates back 3,100 million years and yet its double-layered cell wall is characteristic of modern bacteria. The more visible fossil below is a rod-shaped bacterium that lived about 2,000 million years ago. Life on other planets may have evolved—or may now exist—in similar rudimentary form.

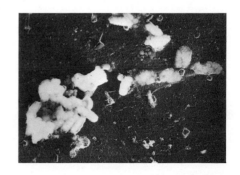

ing the earth an atmosphere composed predominantly of steam. Because of the greater pressure of the steam-filled atmosphere, the temperature required to evaporate the ocean would have to be considerably higher than the present boiling point of water. Geophysicists do not expect this temperature to be reached, at least for a very long time, but they agree that the extensive film of liquid water on most of the earth's surface is an unusual borderline phenomenon not likely to be found on other planets in our solar system.

The atmosphere's lowest-gaseous layer, the troposphere extending to about 35,000 feet, is the familiar air that living creatures breathe and through which most aeroplanes fly. When clouds are absent, nearly all the visible light in sunlight passes through the troposphere to the ground and raises its temperature. The ground tries to give this energy back to space by its own radiation, but its comparatively low temperature permits it to radiate only infra-red light whose wave length is very much longer than most of the radiation emitted by the sun. Like the glass of a greenhouse, the troposphere is not transparent to infra-red radiation of such a long wave length. The small amounts of water vapour and carbon dioxide that it contains absorb infra-red light and use it to heat the air at low levels. This "greenhouse effect" is one of the reasons why the air is warmer near the earth than it is higher up.

Heat engine at the equator

Another reason is that the ground heats the base of the troposphere by contact. This kind of heating is strongest near the equator, so the troposphere gets hottest there. The air rises, flows towards the Poles and is replaced by cooler air moving horizontally from temperate latitudes. This equatorial "heat engine" is the primary cause of the intricately swirling winds that meteorologists must disentangle to understand the weather. Winds are probably blowing on other planets, produced by the same or similar heating effects.

The top of the troposphere is called the tropopause, and above it is a relatively motionless zone, the mesosphere. Convection currents rarely rise into it, so it gets little heat from below and contains little water vapour. Its most important constituent is a small amount of ozone, an active form of oxygen whose molecules (O_3) are made out of ordinary oxygen (O_2) that has been broken up by ultra-violet light. Ozone is violently poisonous, so it is just as well that it stays in the mesosphere, but it also has a beneficial effect on the earth's life. It strongly absorbs a kind of ultra-violet radiation that would kill all the earth's contemporary organisms, if unprotected, by destroying the vital nucleic acid in their cells.

There is only a trace of ozone in the whole atmosphere. The total amount is equivalent to a layer one one-hundredth of an inch thick at surface pressure, but without it all life on earth would have to stay out of the light, or die. If other planets lack an ozone or an equivalent atmospheric screen, any life that has developed upon them must have found some different protection against the deadly rays contained in sunlight.

Above the ozone layer are other levels of the atmosphere that absorb ultra-violet light, and some of them are ionized, containing large numbers of free electrons knocked off their atoms by energy from the sun. These layers reflect certain kinds of radio waves, guiding them around the earth and so permitting them to be used in long-distance communication.

The never-returning atoms

The outermost zone of the atmosphere is the exosphere, starting at 300 miles. The air at this altitude is so thin that its atoms seldom collide with one another, as they do hundreds of millions of times per second at surface density. Instead they follow ballistic courses like artillery shells, curving high and then down again. Some are on orbits around the earth and are true satellites. The fastest of all, those that have received extra-powerful boosts from violent collisions with other atoms, achieve escape velocity. They soar out of the atmosphere into space and never return to the earth. Most of the defectors are hydrogen atoms separated from water molecules by photo-dissociation. They are not numerous. About one pound of hydrogen escapes from the earth per second, which is not a significant amount on the geologic time scale, and the loss is partly made up by protons, the nuclei of hydrogen atoms, arriving from the sun.

The exosphere frays out gradually, with more and more of its atoms on their way towards permanent escape. Above the base of the exosphere lie the Van Allen radiation belts, the streams of spiralling protons and electrons which have come from the sun and have been trapped by the earth's magnetism. They were discovered by early U.S. satellites and are considered serious hazards for manned space flight at certain altitudes. These belts and the earth's magnetic field extend to about 40,000 miles from the earth; there, the charged particles from the sun overwhelm the feeble magnetism of the distant earth. This is the magnetopause, the final frontier between the earth and interplanetary space.

When astronomers study the distant planets, they search eagerly for the slightest clue that suggests a feature of the well-observed earth. The presence of carbon dioxide in a planet's atmosphere indicates that the greenhouse effect is heating the surface below. The presence of ammonia or other reducing gases shows that the planet is in something like the earth's early condition before the development of green, photosynthetic plants. A planet's surface markings, if any are visible, are compared with the earth's in the hope that the forces that drew them can be understood by analogy with the influences understood on earth.

It is known already that the earth is unique in one respect: no other planet has anything to compare with its rich production of radio waves. If the earth were observed with modest radio telescopes from Mars or Venus, it would show as a powerful radio source more brilliant at certain wave lengths than anything else in the sky. This radio flux is of biological origin. It is the ceaseless uproar of man's TV and radio broadcasts, escaping into space through the ionized layers of the upper atmosphere.

A Space Visitor's
View of the Earth

Of the nine planets in the solar system, our own earth is the only one that has been even superficially explored by man. At that, although he has roamed his home planet for a million years, man's first-hand knowledge is limited to a narrow belt extending a few miles above and below the surface. No human eyes have ever seen the earth as it might look from Mars (*opposite*) or have perceived the nickel-iron mass that is believed to make up the earth's core—and which accounts for more than one-eighth of the planet's volume.

Yet what *is* known about the earth can often be cautiously applied to its companions, all of which are assumed to have been similarly born as solidified clouds of dust and gases left over from the creation of the sun. Although no two planets are identical, man can learn important fundamentals about all of them—and perhaps avoid serious mistakes—by studying his handy planet as though it were a foreign body. For the information today's scientists glean about the nature of the earth's atmosphere, structure and forms of life will provide clues to what tomorrow's interplanetary explorers can expect when they venture into the universe.

THE EARTH FROM MARS
The earth, shown as it might look through a telescope from Mars, more than 35 million miles away, appears as a blurry, bluish globe that grows larger and more shadowed as it approaches on its shorter orbit and passes between Mars and the sun. The earth's clouds obscure some features, but the oceans can be distinguished, as can large land masses like South America (*lower left*).

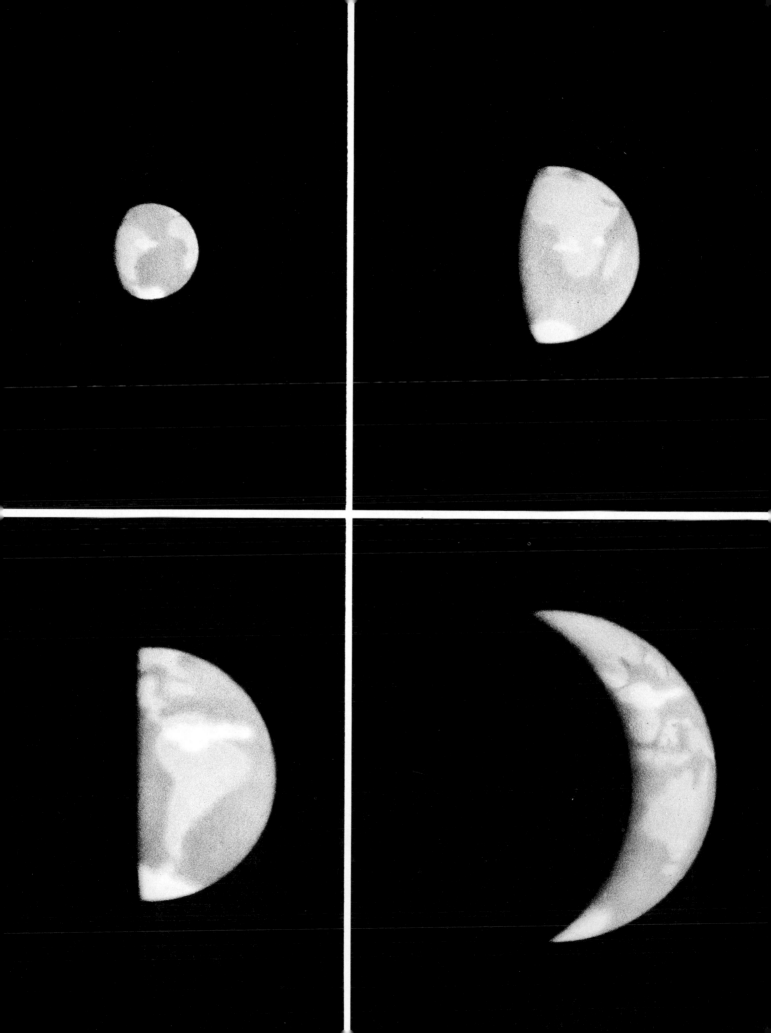

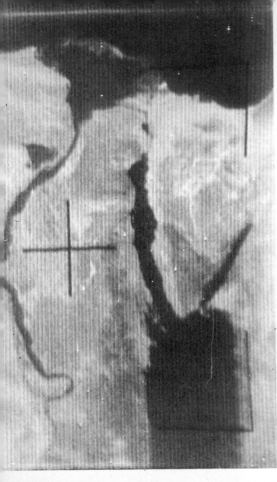

THE EARTH FROM 400 MILES

These photographs, taken by orbiting weather satellites, show the earth as light areas of land near a darker surface. Although the land details are indistinct, the outlines traced by the contrasting areas are very distinct. The Mediterranean Sea, Red Sea and the Nile are all easily identifiable in the cloudless view of Egypt (*left*). The Eastern Seaboard of the United States is clearly visible, below, from Maine (*upper right*) to Delaware Bay (*lower left*), while the British Isles (*right*) can be seen in their entirety.

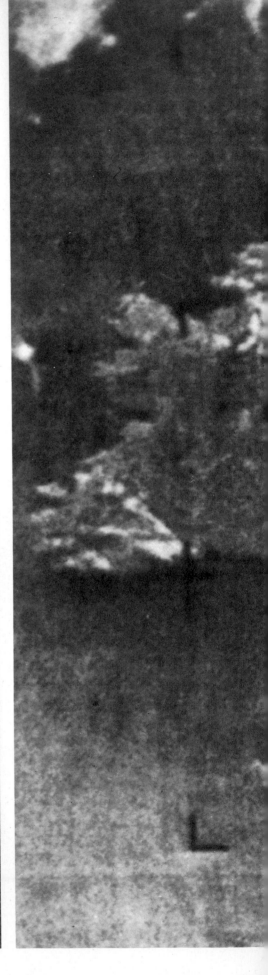

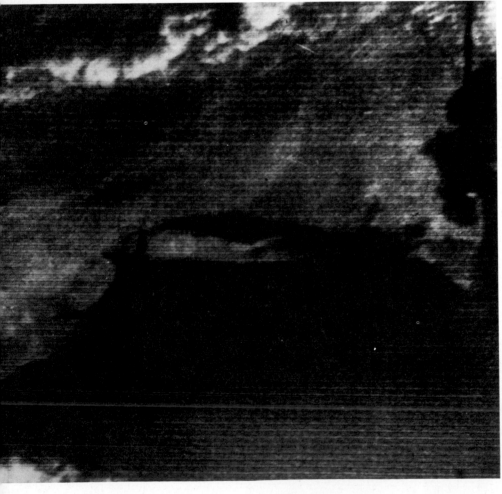

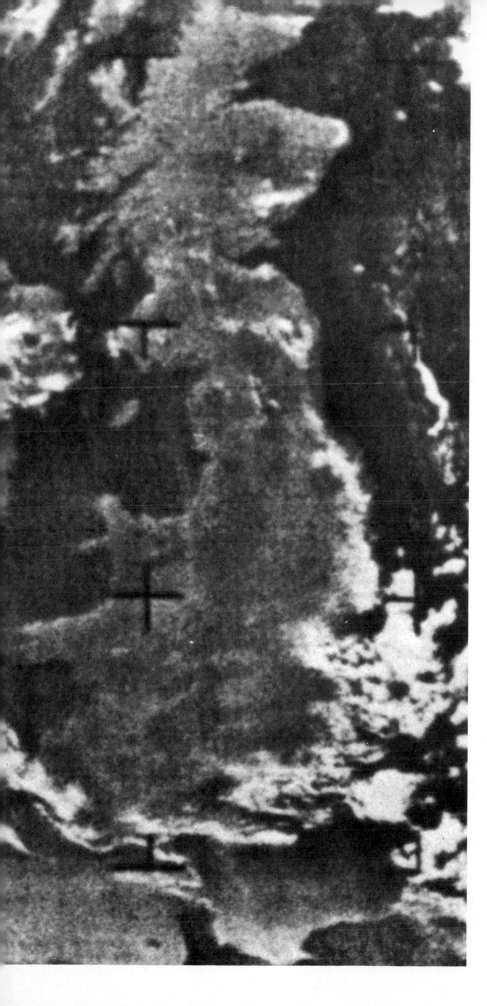

A World of Land and Water

The difficulty of detecting even intelligent life on some other planet is illustrated by these pictures of the earth taken from about 400 miles. Although familiar geography emerges clearly—the river Nile in the view of Egypt (*opposite, top*), the mouth of the river Hudson in the view of the United States' Eastern Seaboard (*opposite, bottom*), and the English Channel in the picture of the British Isles (*left*)—the three great cities that should be seen in these pictures (Cairo, New York and London) are invisible, as are bridges, railways and other man-made works.

While it is impossible to determine the presence of life from pictures like these—similar photographs of Mars were taken from 8,160 miles away by Mariner IV in 1965, and from about 2,130 miles away by Mariners VI and VII in 1969 and from 800 miles away by Mariner IX in 1971—the contrast between dark and bright areas implies different surfaces. One of them could be water, which seems essential to the formation of earth-like life, though not necessarily to other kinds that may exist elsewhere.

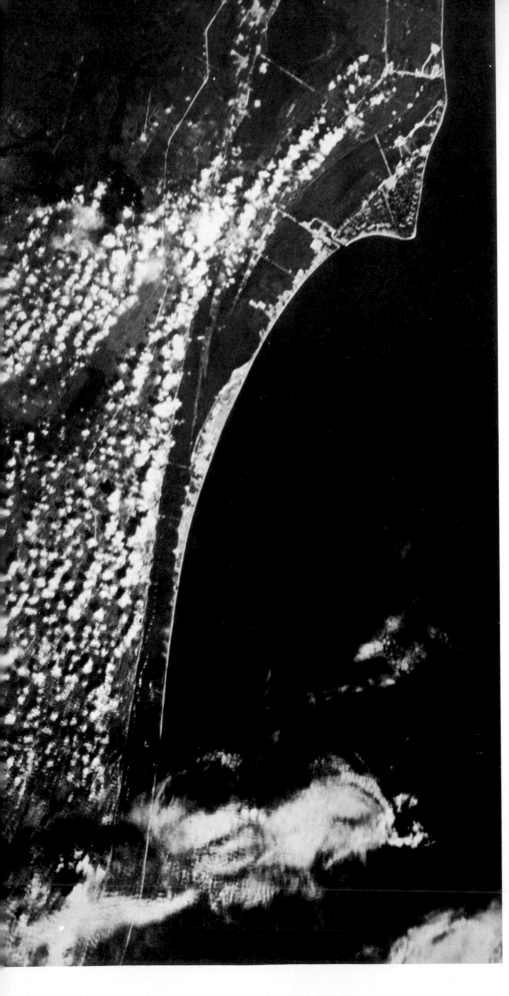

Signs of Life from 150 Miles Up

It will probably not be necessary for a space explorer actually to set foot on a planet to determine if anything like a human society exists there. He may be able to prove this with a hand-held camera from 150 miles if his view is not obscured by clouds. From this elevation, he could see panoramas as detailed as these on the earth, in which bridges, roads, farms, even rocket launching pads, are clearly visible. Unnatural straight lines and geometric patterns, like those at Cape Kennedy (*left*), would instantly indicate the presence of an advanced civilization.

A man gazing down through the earth's blue haze—caused by the atmosphere reflecting back the blue component of sunlight—at Southern California's Imperial Valley (*right*) can distinguish not only man-made squares, but also evidence of folding in the rock structure of the mountains.

A LONG LOOK AT CAPE KENNEDY
This picture of the 100-mile-long Canaveral Peninsula, its Cape Kennedy launching pads visible at the upper right, was taken in 1965 from Gemini V, orbiting 150 miles above the earth. The white puffs are an earth phenomenon: cumulus clouds that form only over land.

HIGH ABOVE A DESERT VALLEY
California's Imperial Valley and Salton Sea, as seen from Gemini V (partially visible at the lower left), lie in a basin-like depression created by ancient earth faults. Most of the squares on the right are cotton and alfalfa farms, while in the far background the State of Arizona is visible.

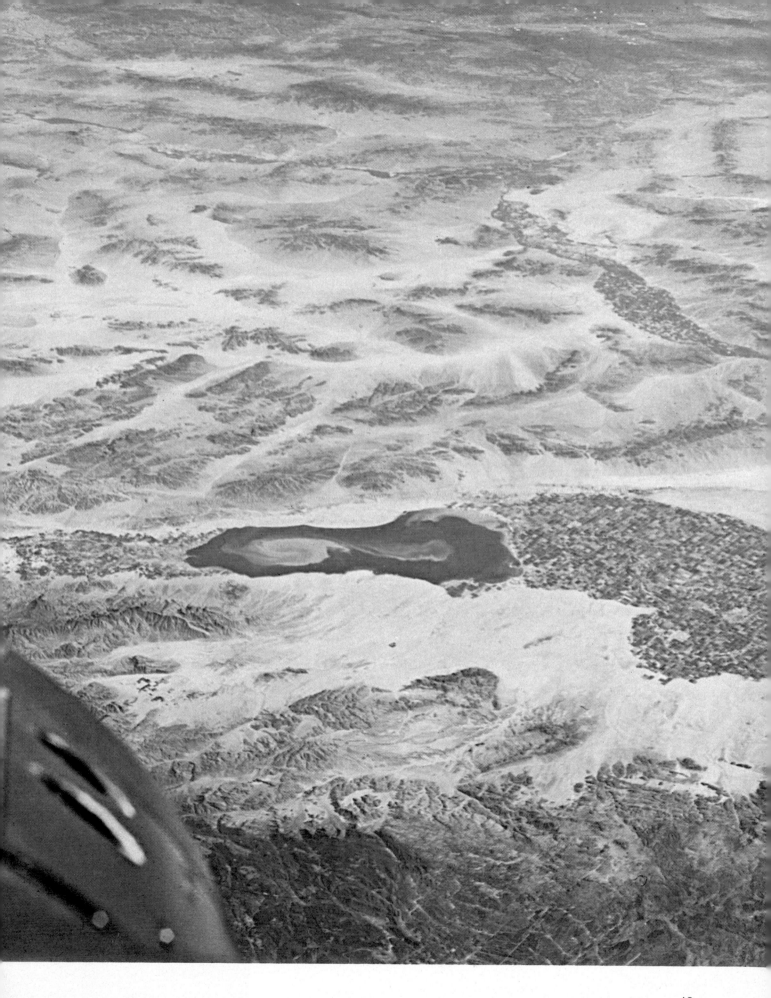

An Ice City
That Never Was

If men judged planets by their first appearances, they would be just as wrong as Christopher Columbus was when he landed in the Antilles and thought he was in the Orient.

The picture above, an earthly version of a scene like one that might be transmitted by a "soft-landed" planet exploratory vehicle, is open to two misinterpretations. The first, which no trained scientist would make, is to translate the shapes in the background into the skyline of a city like

San Francisco (*right*). The second, and more reasonable error, is to assume that such a bleak and desolate vista is typical of an entire planet. But just as the earth can produce ice packs and jungles within a relatively limited temperature range, so other planets can be expected to present equally contrasting terrains. Astronomers long ago observed ice caps on Mars; they are now known to be a thin ice frost or a thicker covering of frozen carbon dioxide (dry ice).

THROUGH A VISITOR'S EYES

The deserted Antarctic panorama above would probably puzzle a visitor from another planet. He might not recognize either the water or the ice for what they really are. At a brief glance —such as might be obtained by "soft-landed" cameras—he might very easily equate the similar patterns of breaking-up ice in the distance and hillside homes in San Francisco (*left*), and conclude that he was seeing the same phenomenon. He might become even more confused if he noticed the single visible clue to life that appears amid the expanse of frozen desolation —the set of penguin tracks in the foreground.

The Seasons
of a Tilted World

What an interplanetary visitor to the earth—or any other heavenly body—saw around him might depend not only on where he landed but on when he landed there. The earth's face alters radically from season to season.

Seasons result from a fixed tilt in the earth's axis, which turns the Poles alternately towards the sun. Above the Arctic Circle, frozen tundra (*bottom*) flowers in July, when the sun shines 24 hours daily. In the winterless equatorial zone, jungles and rain forests (*right*) flourish. Between the extremes are the temperate zones, where the changing beauty of trees (*far right*) reflects the seasons.

A SUDDEN SUMMER
The treeless tundra of the Canadian Arctic, some 1,000 miles below the North Pole, comes alive briefly but spectacularly in the summer. Because of the earth's tilt, the sun then shines almost constantly, thawing the frozen ground and giving life to some 900 species of flowers.

TREES FOR ALL SEASONS

The jungle-like rain forest of Brazil (*left*), a product of a hot climate and tropical trade winds, probably could not survive a freeze and may never have to. In temperate zones, however, trees react to seasonal temperature changes. In the pictures above, the flowering apple tree of an Austrian spring, the silvery birches of a French autumn and the snowy pines of an American winter all share this adaptability. A series of regular but unexplainable brightness changes on Mars has been interpreted as a sign of the changing seasons on that planet.

The Many Faces of Life on Earth

Some scientists think that 100,000 million planets capable of supporting life exist in the Milky Way. But the impossibility of predicting the forms such life might take is demonstrated by the variety and unpredictability of life on earth. More than 4,000 million years of evolution have produced several million distinct types of living flora and fauna within the earth's atmosphere. These range from microscopic bacteria to 100-foot whales, from man to the Australian platypus, an evolutional oddity which is an egg-laying mammal possessing the bill and webbed feet of a duck and the tail of a beaver. As on earth, life on other planets may differ every few miles. The Darwin frog, for example, is found in a single forest of Chile and nowhere else, although the earth contains many similar forests.

THE RESULTS OF EVOLUTION

Each living earth creature seen here has something in common with the others: the basic chemistry of its life processes. Except for the nematodes, worms that float in all the earth's oceans, all these creatures are found only in the limited areas indicated—a sign that a wide variety of life is possible and that completely different types may exist on other planets

BASKET GRASS: TEXAS

DWARF COCONUT TREE: KOH SAMUI ISLAND

TIGER: ASIA

DARWIN FROG: VALDIVIA, CHILE

GREEN PYTHON: NEW GUINEA

LLAMA: ANDES MOUNTAINS

GOOSE BARNACLES: CALIFORNIA AND OREGON

ELEPHANT'S EAR: JAVA

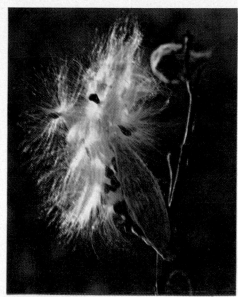
MILKWEED: EASTERN UNITED STATES

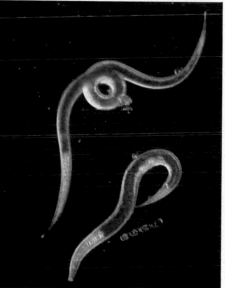
NEMATODES: ALL OCEANS

GRAMA: WEST INDIAN WATERS

TENREC: MALAGASY

SILK SPIDER: THAILAND

WHITE-LIPPED GARDEN SNAIL: EASTERN UNITED STATES

CASSOWARY: NORTHERN AUSTRALIA

55

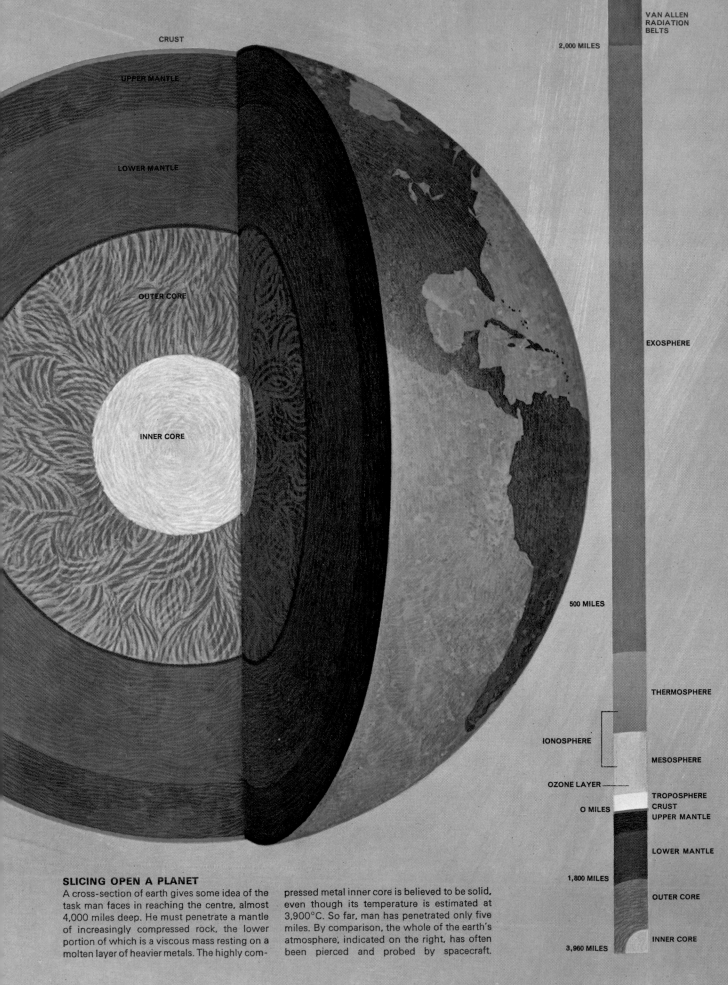

CRUST

UPPER MANTLE

LOWER MANTLE

OUTER CORE

INNER CORE

VAN ALLEN
RADIATION
BELTS

2,000 MILES

EXOSPHERE

500 MILES

THERMOSPHERE

IONOSPHERE

MESOSPHERE

OZONE LAYER

TROPOSPHERE
CRUST
UPPER MANTLE

O MILES

LOWER MANTLE

1,800 MILES

OUTER CORE

INNER CORE

3,960 MILES

SLICING OPEN A PLANET

A cross-section of earth gives some idea of the task man faces in reaching the centre, almost 4,000 miles deep. He must penetrate a mantle of increasingly compressed rock, the lower portion of which is a viscous mass resting on a molten layer of heavier metals. The highly com-pressed metal inner core is believed to be solid, even though its temperature is estimated at 3,900°C. So far, man has penetrated only five miles. By comparison, the whole of the earth's atmosphere, indicated on the right, has often been pierced and probed by spacecraft.

The Skies Above, the Earth Below

To help man in forming meaningful conclusions about the composition of other planets, he must fully explore the last two frontiers of the earth—straight up and straight down.

The rockets, balloons and satellites of space technology have unlocked many mysteries of the atmosphere. As the indicator opposite shows, the road to space—and to interplanetary travel—is well charted. Above the familiar region of breathable air—the troposphere—lies the mesosphere, whose lowest layer contains a screen of ozone molecules that filter out the sun's ultra-violet rays. Extending from the mesosphere into the adjacent thermosphere is the ionosphere, with its flickering auroras and luminous clouds. The exosphere begins about 300 miles up and extends to include the Van Allen belts—a huge region of charged particles that are trapped by the magnetic attraction of the earth.

Far less is known about the composition of the earth itself. In 1909 Andrija Mohorovičić found an abrupt velocity change in seismic waves, indicating a clear division between the earth's rocky crust and its heavier underlying mantle. But man has yet to penetrate physically the Mohorovičić discontinuity—better known as the Moho. It is mostly through study of earthquake waves, as well as of subsurface heat-flow measurements and magnetic surveys, that scientists have constructed the cross-section opposite: a metallic inner core with a radius of about 800 miles surrounded by a molten outer core 1,300 miles thick and a crystalline mantle about 1,800 miles thick. Compared to these magnitudes, the earth's crust, only five to 25 miles deep, is a very thin skin. And the earth's ocean trenches and high mountain chains are mere lumps and wrinkles on its surface.

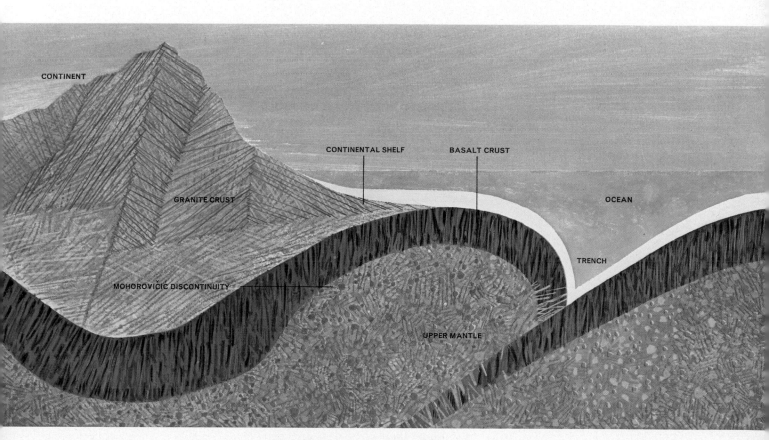

EARTH'S LUMPS AND WRINKLES

Surface features of the earth—five-mile-high mountains, seven-mile-deep ocean trenches—are lumps and wrinkles on its thinnest layer, the crust. It is hard, heavy basalt supporting lumps of lighter granite, the mountains and continents. Under such a granite mass the ba-salt thickens and dips, then thins and rises to the continental shelf only to drop into a trench. In the trench above, the basalt bottom, or Mohorovičić discontinuity, is broken by basalt being forced down into the mantle, propelled by stirrings in the earth's interior (*overleaf*).

A Constantly Changing Planet

Ever since its birth in spinning star dust about 5,000 million years ago, the earth has been changing. There are tremendous forces at work deep in its interior, powerful enough to rip open the earth's crust and to move continents about like drifting icebergs.

The continent-moving forces are generated within the earth's mantle by a circular flow of hot rock (*below*), which oozes through the crust at a globe-girding rift, a split in the undersea mountain chain called the Mid-Ocean Ridge. Here the rising rock joins the crust and pushes it away from the ridge, thereby inching continents east and west.

The convection-caused shifting of crust seems to explain the evolution of the earth. Originally there was a single land mass that began breaking up 3,000 million years ago into two continents, Laurasia and Gondwanaland (*top, right*). These broke up into the shapes we know today (*centre*). In 10 million years the world may resemble the map at bottom, right —with California drifting out to sea, Florida linked to South America, and Africa moving away from Eurasia.

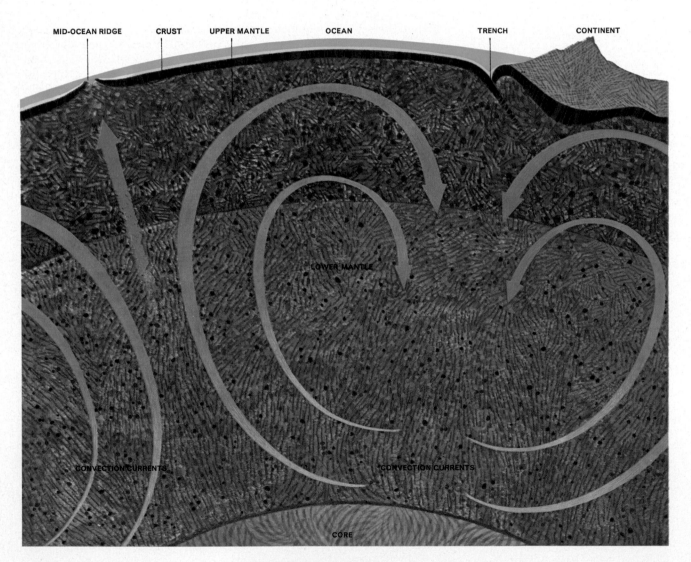

MID-OCEAN RIDGE   CRUST   UPPER MANTLE   OCEAN   TRENCH   CONTINENT

LOWER MANTLE

CONVECTION CURRENTS   CONVECTION CURRENTS

CORE

THE DRIFTING CONTINENTS

The shifting of land masses of the earth —evidenced, for example, by the slippage of California coastlands into the Pacific at a rate of two inches per year—is now traced to a convectional flow of hot material within the mantle. This flow sustains a continuing interchange of rock between mantle and crust. Ascending currents squeeze rock out of the mantle and into the crust, principally at a long crack in the Mid-Ocean Ridge. Crust sections are forced sideways, shifting the continents. But where crust sections encounter a continental mass, the sections buckle to form a deep trench, through which they slide down and return to currents in the mantle. This steady recirculation could one day lead to a strange new world (*right*).

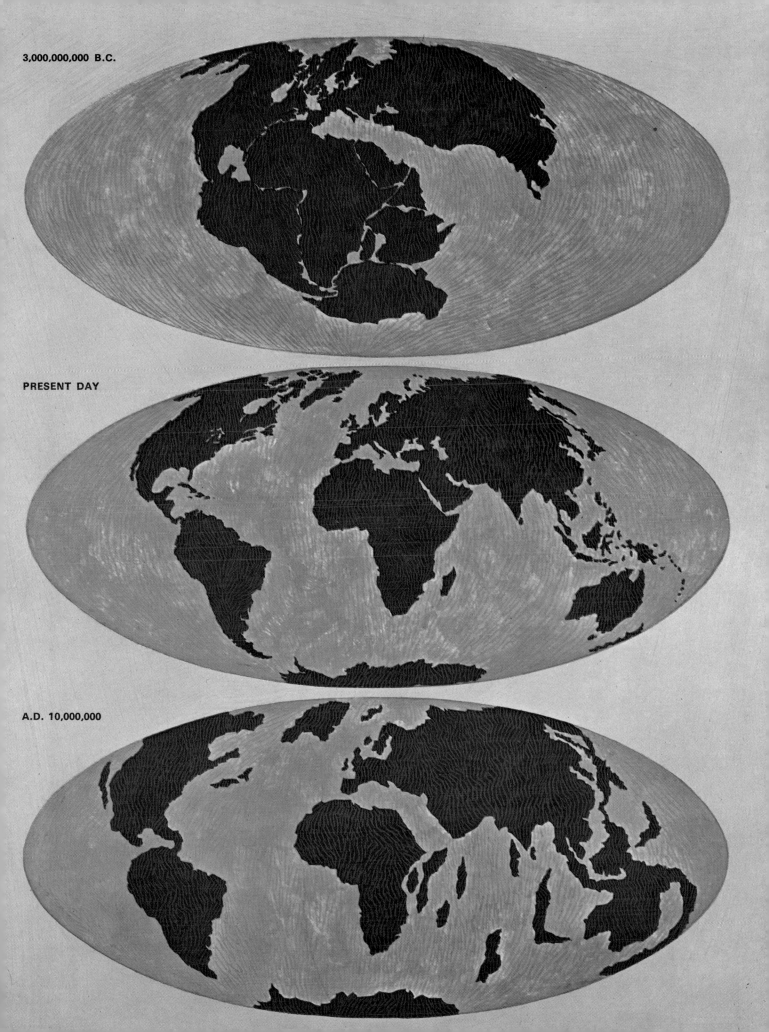

3,000,000,000 B.C.

PRESENT DAY

A.D. 10,000,000

3

Measuring the Distant Spheres

Galileo's 1609 telescopes, the first widely used in astronomy, magnified up to 20 times.

ONE OF THE GREAT ACHIEVEMENTS of the human intellect is the surprisingly intimate knowledge of the planets that has been deduced simply by studying them, with one device or another, from many millions of miles away. Although the rapid improvement of space technology is now beginning to make first-hand study possible, for many years to come the great bulk of information about the solar system will continue to be derived from electromagnetic waves that cross the vacuum of space needing no vehicle or medium in which to travel.

Fortunately these talented waves exist in great variety, each kind with its special usefulness. Visible light is one part, but only a small part, of the electromagnetic spectrum. At one end of the spectrum are radio waves many miles long; at the other end are gamma rays whose waves are shorter than one thousand-millionth of an inch. Between these extremes, in order of decreasing wave length, are the shorter radio waves and microwaves used in communication; infra-red light of many kinds; ordinary visible light, ultra-violet light and X-rays. Although waves of different lengths come from different sources and have different characteristics, they all travel at the same velocity—186,000 miles per second—and they all yield information if disentangled with skill and subtlety.

In the detailed observation of the planets the naked human eye is not much use. It is a masterpiece of evolution and beautifully designed for its natural purpose, which is to keep its owner in touch with his rapidly changing surroundings, but for most kinds of astronomy it is a blunt instrument. The visible light to which it is sensitive is only a tiny segment of the electromagnetic spectrum. The eye is totally blind to all the rest. Its ability to separate close sources of light and thereby to see fine details, called its resolving power, is coarse. Many familiar stars, such as Mizar in the Big Dipper, show themselves to be double in the simplest telescope. The eye sees them as single because it fails to resolve objects that are closer together than one minute of arc, which is one-thirtieth of the angular diameter of the full moon. It is a marvel of human ingenuity that the general plan of the solar system was worked out so correctly by the naked eye before the appearance of the telescope, to which astronomy owes its rapid modern advance.

The telescope was the product of Dutch spectacle makers who had been grinding lenses for generations without understanding quite how they worked. A few years after 1600 one of them, possibly a man named Lippershey, discovered by happy accident that two lenses of the proper curvature, held the proper distance apart, make distant objects look larger. Galileo was the first to put the fascinating invention to serious work in astronomy.

Galileo's instruments were crude; the first one had a magnification of about three diameters. But when he turned them on the sky in 1609, they vastly enlarged and enriched the universe known to man. Marvel after marvel streamed through the little tube. Among the first major discoveries were the four bright satellites of Jupiter. Venus, his next triumph, proved to have phases like the moon's. He well understood the importance of what he was doing. "I am quite beside myself with wonder," he wrote to a friend in 1610, "and I am infinitely grateful to God that it has pleased Him to permit me to discover such great marvels as were unknown to all preceding centuries."

Modern telescopes, particularly the larger ones, may use curved mirrors instead of lenses, but they all operate on the same optical principles and they all perform two services. First, they improve the eye's resolving power, its ability to see fine details. The objective (front) lens forms at its focus an upside-down image whose size depends on its distance beyond the lens. The image can be made directly visible by putting a sheet of frosted glass at the focus. The picture is generally very small, but it is a captive in the telescope tube and can be examined by an eye lens that acts as a microscope and enlarges it to any desirable size, just as a regular microscope turns a barely visible insect into an armoured monster. The image of Mars, which looks like a small reddish dot, can be magnified enough for its spread-out markings to be seen separately by the coarse-grained human eye.

Squeezing light for the eye

The second service of a telescope is to gather light. The pupil of the eye is never more than one-third of an inch in diameter, and all the light available to it must pass through this small opening. A telescope's objective lens is the equivalent of the eye's pupil. The difference is that it is larger and therefore gathers more light, and it packs this light into a bright bundle of rays slender enough to enter the pupil, thus making available to the eye more of the light emitted by the source. This makes objects look proportionately brighter. The 200-inch aperture of California's Mount Palomar telescope, the world's largest, concentrates 360,000 times as much light as the eye; if it were pointed at the sun and used as a burning glass (which is not likely), it would melt a sizable hole in a firebrick.

Telescopes as such, no matter how large and well designed, are only the beginning of astronomical technology. Equally important is photography, which improves on the eye's action in additional ways. When photographic film is placed at the focus of a telescope, the whole telescope acts as a camera, and the film makes a permanent record that can be studied at leisure and referred to later.

Even more important, the film's image is not formed in an instant, as the eye's is. It is cumulative, building up like a pencil drawing made blacker by retracing. A telescope-camera can follow all night—or even for several nights—the motion of the same dim object while its feeble light builds up a picture on the film. The spiral arms of galaxies grow, hour by hour, reaching far out into intergalactic space. The most spectacular pictures of the deep sky are made by very long exposures.

Looking at astronomical objects with a telescope or making photographs of them utilizes only a small part of the information contained in light: its direction and its relative intensity, which together form images

GALILEO GALILEI, the great Italian astronomer, pointed his telescope skywards in 1609 and obtained a new view of the universe. In the drawing below, made from precise observations, Galileo verified the theory of Copernicus that Venus has phases like the moon's. Above Venus, from the left, are Saturn, Jupiter and Mars.

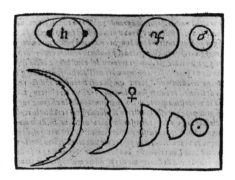

of the objects on the eye's retina or the camera's film. But if light is taken apart into the many wave lengths that it normally contains, other kinds of information can be extracted. To accomplish this analysis, light must be examined with a prism or a grating of finely ruled lines in an instrument called a spectroscope, to which man owes an important part of his knowledge of the universe.

A rainbow from the planets

Everyone has seen a rainbow, and most people know that when sunlight passes through a prism it spreads out into a rainbow pattern of colours. Each colour contains a group of wave lengths, and together they extend from the shortest waves in the visible violet to the longest in the red. The colours as seen by the eye do not yield much information because the eye is not equipped to distinguish small differences in wave length. But if sunlight is passed through a narrow slit and then spread out by a prism, its rainbow spectrum is crossed by thousands of bright or dark lines. Each line is an image of the slit in light of a slightly different wave length, and each has a story to tell about the place it came from.

The bright and dark lines are a cryptogram that science has learned to interpret with great precision. When a gas, for instance, is heated to such an extent that it gives out visible light, that light is concentrated in a limited number of wave lengths, so when it is examined with a spectroscope it separates into a spectrum which is made up of individual bright lines. These spectra are different for different chemical elements. The bright lines they contain—their number, relative brightness and specific wave lengths—identify the element just as positively as finger-prints are capable of identifying a man. When a known pattern, or a recognizable portion of one, is found in a spectrum, the element responsible can be identified. And often an estimate can be made of its abundance in the source of light.

The dark lines have a closely related origin. Under certain conditions an element is capable of absorbing light instead of emitting it. The wave lengths it absorbs are the same as those that it can emit. Thus when a spectroscope analyses light that has been partially absorbed by a substance while passing through or reflecting off it, a second type of spectrum is obtained. This absorption spectrum consists of dark lines, and they create a pattern identical to the pattern of the bright lines emitted by the element.

By comparing these sequences of bright or dark lines with the spectra obtained from known substances on earth, astronomers can tell what stars are made of. This same technique can be applied to the planets, although not quite so readily as to stars, since planets give no visible light of their own, merely shining by reflected sunlight. But materials in their atmospheres or on their surfaces do absorb parts of the solar spectrum, and so betray to some extent their chemical composition. If any proof is needed that the moon is not made of green cheese, spectroscopy supplies it.

Planets are comparatively cool and so emit little radiation of their own. That which they do emit is almost entirely infra-red. Astronomers can turn a telescope on a planet and measure with delicate instruments the degree to which detectors here on earth are heated by certain selected infra-red wave lengths emitted by the planet. The "infra-red brightness temperature" of the planet can then be computed. It is the temperature that the planet must have in order to deliver to the earth the amount of infra-red power that the instruments have detected. This temperature might refer to the planetary surface or the cloud layer, depending on which is the source of the infra-red radiation emitted to space.

The waves that tell so much about planets must pass through the earth's atmosphere before telescopes convert them into spectra and images. That trip is, for many of the waves, a rough one. Astronomers, as people, may admire the blue of the sky and derive pleasure from sunset clouds, but in a professional way they find the atmosphere an annoyance. They think of it as a stifling blanket that shuts off most of the information that the universe is trying to feed into their instruments. Worse, it is a moving blanket; it crawls and writhes with turbulence like the air above a hot pavement and distorts the light that manages to struggle through.

When the stars dance

Even the clearest nights, when the sky is velvety black and the stars sparkle like jewels, are often useless for serious observing. Star images dance like gnats, and the markings on the faces of planets merge into shimmering blurs. Astronomers call this condition "bad seeing". It can be avoided to some extent by putting observatories on mountain-tops in arid regions, where clouds are infrequent and much of the turbulent atmosphere is left below. But even in the best positions, bad seeing sets a limit on the finest telescopes.

Because of bad seeing, the direct human eye still has an honoured place in planetary astronomy. Photographing a planet, even with a large telescope, needs a considerable exposure time during which atmospheric turbulence smears the image and obscures fine details. But the quick-seeing eye of a human observer at a telescope can watch a planet night after night, waiting for rare intervals when the atmosphere happens to be steady. Then for an enchanted instant the face of the planet comes uncannily clear. Tantalizing markings spring into view, and quickly fade again. If the observer is trained and skilled, he can sketch some of these features before they disappear.

Even if the atmosphere were always perfectly steady, it would still be a barrier. The air on a clear, bright day looks transparent because the eye is sensitive only to certain wave lengths of electromagnetic radiation —those of visible light—that are not absorbed. To other kinds of radiation the atmosphere is as opaque as heavy smoke. Astronomers describe this condition in a rather curious way by saying that the light the eye sees passes through the "visible window" in the atmosphere.

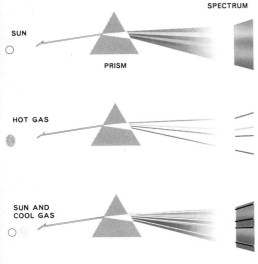

SPECTRUM

SUN

PRISM

HOT GAS

SUN AND
COOL GAS

SPLITTING LIGHT into its component colours —a technique called spectroscopy—is one method astronomers use to identify atmospheric molecules on distant planets. When the light comes from dense hot gas, like the sun, a prism separates it into a wide spectrum of colours (shown at the top as shades of blue) with each colour representing specific wave lengths of light. A luminous, less dense gas (*centre*) emits only a few wave lengths, producing a widely separated spectrum. But when the same gas is cool and sunlight passes through, its molecules absorb the wave lengths they would normally emit, and the resulting spectrum has dark lines, which allow astronomers to identify the molecules in the gas.

The atmosphere might be compared to an opaque barrier laid over the entire spectrum of electromagnetic waves. In this barrier are openings, or windows, each corresponding to a specific range of wave lengths at different parts of the spectrum. One of these windows admits visible light; another admits a particular group of infra-red wave lengths. Wave lengths that fall between the windows do not get through.

These varieties of light are detected and recorded by astronomers with techniques that are roughly analogous to the way the human eye responds to visible light. But the atmosphere has another broad window, and through it come waves that must be treated in an entirely different manner. No known earthly creature has natural sense organs that take advantage of them. These waves are so long that they are radio waves and they must be "seen" with a radio receiver.

The radio window

In 1931 Karl Jansky, an American physicist, was investigating a kind of radio noise or static that interferes with long-distance radio communication. The noise was caused by radiation that was familiar in wave length, but he found it was coming from outside the atmosphere. Jansky's discovery marked the birth of radio astronomy, which is now a technique almost as important as astronomical observation through the visible and infra-red windows.

The radio window in the atmosphere does not permit all radio waves from space to reach the earth's surface. Microwaves of wave length appreciably shorter than one centimetre (0.4 inch, used in some radars) are absorbed by water vapour in the atmosphere. If the waves are longer than about 15 metres, they are reflected back into space by the same electrically charged layers that guide man-made radio waves around the curve of the earth. But the radiation between one centimetre and 15 metres, which does pass through the radio window, brings a wide variety of information not provided by optical astronomy.

Radio telescopes are fundamentally different from optical ones. They do not form an image of the planet or other object at which they are pointed. Usually they concentrate radio waves from the planet as a whole on a detector so that the intensity of the radiation at various times can be recorded in some handy form such as a wavy line on a moving strip of paper. Often the telescope remains fixed and the earth's rotation swings it across the sky until it points directly at a source of radio waves. A large peak then appears among numerous lesser waves on the paper. The height of the peak tells how much radio energy is being received from the source at the wave length to which the telescope is tuned. The mere existence of the radio-signal peak proves that *something* is out there— a fact that in many cases can be established in no other way—and its wave length may hint at what the something is. But most important, the strength of the peak can be used to calculate the temperature of the object. In this way radio telescopes serve as thermometers. They also detect the presence of magnetic fields by noting the radiation given off

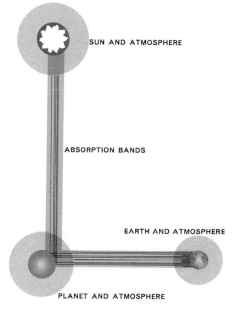

ABSORPTION LINES patterned by molecular activity (*opposite page*), are studied by astronomers for clues to a distant planet's atmosphere. Sunlight (*blue*), with some of its wave lengths already absorbed by the solar atmosphere (*dark lines*), reflects off the planet's surface, gaining more dark lines as other wave lengths are absorbed by the planet's atmosphere. Still more lines appear as the light passes through the earth's atmosphere. Confronted with a spectrum whose dark lines represent absorption by three different atmospheres, astronomers eliminate the lines known to be contributed by the sun and the earth. The rest can be used to identify the gases of the planet's atmosphere.

SUN AND ATMOSPHERE

ABSORPTION BANDS

EARTH AND ATMOSPHERE

PLANET AND ATMOSPHERE

by the charged particles moving within the fields.

For studying the planets, radio astronomy is proving extremely useful, making up to a considerable extent for the fact that planets do not emit visible light of their own. The materials the planets are made of emit radio waves. And these waves, unlike visible light, easily penetrate planetary atmospheres and cloud layers. The first evidence that the temperature of the surface of Venus exceeded 300°C. was detected by the radio telescope of the United States Naval Research Laboratory, Washington D.C., in 1956. The belts of high-speed charged particles that surround Jupiter, similar to the earth's Van Allen belts, were a mystery until the radio waves they emit were traced to their source by two 90-foot radio telescopes at California Institute of Technology.

To the moon and back in 2.6 seconds

The traffic in radio astronomy is not all one-way. The great dish-shaped antennae used to collect signals from space can also be used as powerful radars to send waves into space and then listen for echoes reflected from anything they hit. The moon is an easy target for this sort of probing. A wave goes out and bounces back in 2.6 seconds as a strong signal. These waves first proved that the lunar surface is not steep and rugged. Radar bounced off Venus or Mars takes several minutes to make the round trip, and the reflected waves are extremely weak when they reach the earth. But by accurately timing these faint echoes, radio astronomers can now sense prominences on planetary surfaces and even follow them as they rotate with the planets. Already this kind of radar surveying has revealed what seem to be mountains on Venus, and has settled a long-standing dispute about Mercury; that planet does not, as had been thought, keep the same face permanently towards the sun. Radar astronomy is developing rapidly. It is the only way (short of a space voyage) that planets can be subjected to active probing, not mere passive observing, and great future discoveries are hoped for it.

Astronomers are duly grateful for their radio window, but they still are not satisfied. They would like to stop peering through windows and get out into the great outdoors. Beyond the atmosphere the whole electromagnetic spectrum from gamma rays to mile-long radio waves bombards the earth from space, criss-crossing in every direction and loaded with information about undreamed-of wonders. Much of this treasure does not penetrate the atmosphere and is therefore beyond the reach of ground observatories. The hopes of many forward-looking astronomers centre on establishing observatories outside the atmosphere, a step that may be as fruitful as the invention of the telescope or the development of radio astronomy.

This is not an easy task; astronomical instruments are both large and

ELECTROMAGNETIC WAVES indicated by the wavy lines in this schematic drawing, are emitted by the sun and, to a lesser extent, by the planets. While the great majority of radiation wave lengths are blocked by the earth's atmosphere, certain wave lengths are admitted through atmospheric "windows" (*blue shading*). From these limited ranges of radiation astronomers have gained almost all their information about planets. Optical telescopes collect most of the rays entering through the "optical window", which admits the light we see and extends slightly beyond into neighbouring wave lengths. The longer wave lengths coming through the "infra-red window" can be recorded by special heat detectors, while the even longer wave lengths of the "radio window" require radio receivers. Other wave lengths may be examined only by means of equipment lifted above the earth's atmosphere.

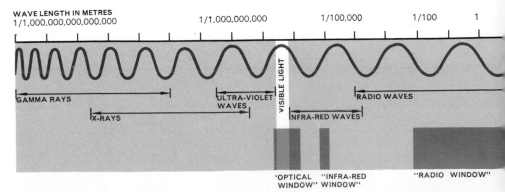

WAVE LENGTH IN METRES
1/1,000,000,000,000,000   1/1,000,000,000   1/100,000   1/100   1

GAMMA RAYS   ULTRA-VIOLET WAVES   VISIBLE LIGHT   RADIO WAVES

X-RAYS   INFRA-RED WAVES

"OPTICAL WINDOW"   "INFRA-RED WINDOW"   "RADIO WINDOW"

delicate, and most of them require extremely steady pointing. But a good start has been made. Telescopes and other instruments of moderate size have been lifted by giant balloons into the upper atmosphere, leaving far below all the turbulence that causes bad seeing as well as almost all the water vapour and most of the carbon dioxide that block important regions of the spectrum. The first convincing evidence of water vapour on Venus came from infra-red light that was intercepted by a balloon-borne spectrometer before the earth's atmosphere could absorb it.

An orbiting observatory

The simplest way to get instruments above most of the atmosphere where they can avoid most of its absorption is to load them on a rocket and shoot them to an altitude of 50 miles or more. This has been done to record the ultra-violet portions of planets' spectra. Some valuable information has been gained but the rockets do not hold still. A much firmer mount would be provided by a satellite. Once it had settled into its orbit around the earth, it could keep its telescope pointed accurately at the same target for any desired length of time. It would always have perfect seeing, and by proper choice of instruments it could extract information from the entire electromagnetic spectrum. A family of such orbiting astronomical observatories, with 36-inch telescopes or larger, is scheduled to search the skies in the 1970s. Much larger ones—including a radio telescope about 12 miles across—are proposed for the more distant future.

In the case of the moon, the Apollo astronauts got a close-up view of a small part of the surface by actually walking on it. This has not been accomplished for the planets. Much has been learned about them, however, by unmanned spacecraft that cruised near them and transmitted pictures back to earth by radio. Thus, U.S. Mariners VI and VII, which passed within 2,200 miles of Mars in July and August 1969, sent pictures that revealed markings as small as 300 yards across, details several hundred times finer than shown in the best photographs taken by telescopes on the earth. Mariner IX and the Soviet probes Mars 2 and 3, orbiting Mars in late 1971 and early 1972, mapped the Martian surface from as close as 800 miles. The unmanned Soviet Venus and Mars probes also detached small capsules that entered the atmospheres of these planets and returned data to earth.

Such means of getting intimate information about the planets are only the prelude to direct exploration by human observers. The first astronauts to make a landing on Mars, for instance, may not learn very much that is new during their brief and risky visit. But their great scientific contribution will lie in their ability to react to the unforeseen. No instrument designed on the distant earth can exploit new opportunities on these strange worlds as well as human beings can.

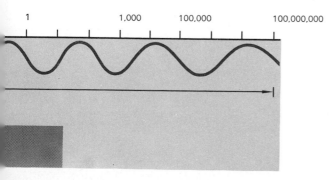

1   1,000   100,000   100,000,000

The Tools
of the Astronomer

The astronomer has always been like a small boy pressing his nose against a sweet-shop window: he could see uncountable tempting delights spread before him, but they were tantalizingly out of reach; he could not smell or taste or touch. As a result, he developed an extraordinary variety of ingenious tools and techniques to help him to sample from a distance. He has used optical telescopes to magnify and brighten the planets so that their features could be examined. Huge radio telescopes have helped him to take the planets' temperatures. With analysing devices he has dissected planetary light and has thus detected the presence of such substances as hydrogen, ammonia and methane.

Within the past few years the space age has partially opened the door to the sweet-shop. Today balloons float almost to the top of the atmosphere for a more distinct view of the heavens, cameras in space craft snap revealing close-up photographs of the moon and Mars. But only now have men finally set foot on a body beyond the earth, and brought back actual samples of its surface to supplement the knowledge so painfully gained from a distance.

A GIANT EAR TO THE SKY
The world's largest fully steerable telescope, at Jodrell Bank in England, listens for radio signals with its 250-foot-wide dish antenna. The dish bounces radar signals off planets and measures their distance from the earth. It was this equipment that first gave Western scientists the pictures transmitted by the Soviet space craft Luna IX after it landed on the moon in February 1966.

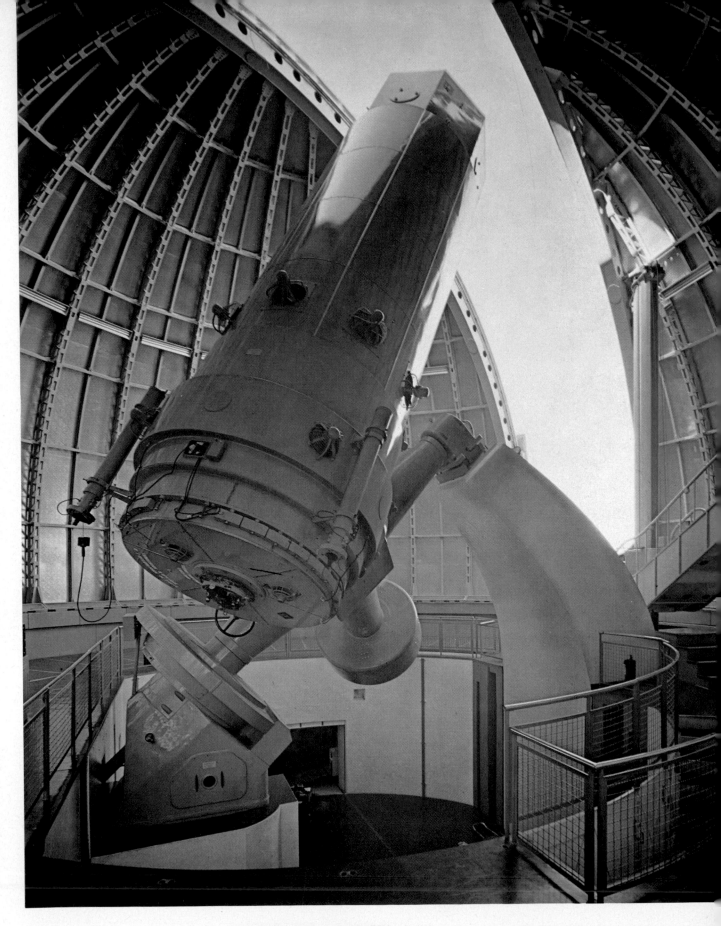

REACHING FOR A RAINBOW

The 76-inch reflecting telescope in Haute Provence, France, has analysed infra-red light from Venus, Mars and Jupiter. Light captured by the instrument passes down through the narrow tube at the lower left to a spectroscope positioned in the basement of the observatory.

The Great Gatherers of Planetary Light

In 1609 Galileo turned a toy-like telescope towards the heavens and, to his delight and amazement, perceived that Jupiter had satellites and Venus displayed phases like the moon's. These were only the first astonishing sights that the telescope's extension of human vision was to provide. Later astronomers would discover the new planets Uranus, Neptune and Pluto, and would detect gases emitted from the moon.

Simple telescopes like Galileo's—a front lens concentrating light into an image that can be viewed with an enlarging lens—are still used. But the great observatories employ huge instruments in which the front lens is replaced by a curved mirror. These mirror telescopes are more effective for studying dim planetary light with another of the major tools of modern astronomy: the spectroscope. This instrument breaks up the light reflected by the planets into identifying patterns, called spectra, which enable scientists to determine the chemical make-up of planets from a distance.

A HUGE EYE TO THE HEAVENS
The giant telescope at Mount Palomar, California, with its 200-inch mirror (in the round, basket-like housing in the lower centre of picture), is the largest on earth. It has been used to measure the temperatures of the surface of Mars and to search for organic matter on the same planet.

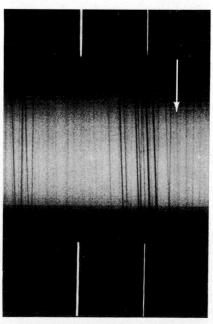

STUDYING THE ATOMS' AUTOGRAPH
In the basement of the Haute Provence observatory, a technician adjusts a spectroscope that is recording the spectrum of light reflected from the planet Jupiter. As the light passes through the instrument, it is separated into its component colours to make the pattern at the right. The dark lines indicate absorption of light by atoms and molecules; the one indicated by an arrow is identified by its position as the line of ammonia.

FOCUSING RAYS FROM SPACE

At the University of Arizona a telescope (*right*) gathers infra-red radiation from the planets with a 60-inch parabolic aluminium mirror (in the housing at the centre). The mirror focuses the radiation on a detector that precisely measures planetary temperatures millions of miles away.

COOLING A HEAT MEASURER

Dr. Frank Low pumps liquid helium into a vacuum bottle housing a device called a germanium bolometer. The instrument is able to detect a hundred-million-millionth of a watt of infra-red radiation, equivalent to sensing the glow of a lighted cigarette 10,000 miles away.

A COOL READING FROM JUPITER

As Dr. Low sights the telescope (*below*) on Jupiter, the germanium bolometer inside the bottle at the centre of the picture registers the distant temperature as a tracing on a chart. This infrared-detection technique has measured temperatures on Saturn and the moon.

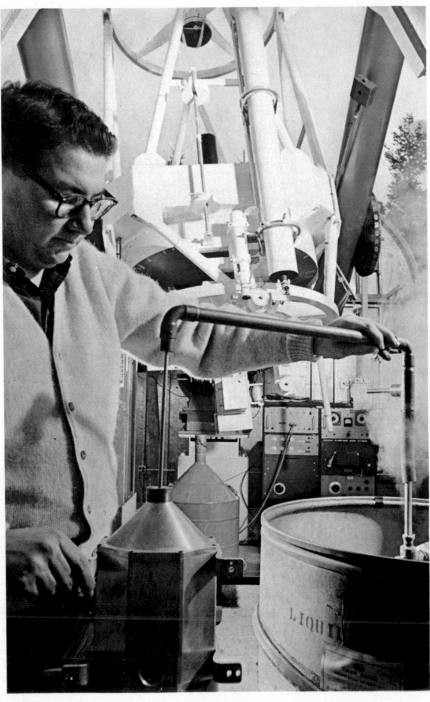

Taking the Planets' Temperatures

With delicate electrical thermometers connected to their telescopes, astronomers have learned that temperatures on the planets are extremely severe. Mercury gets as hot as 420° C., while Pluto may be as cold as −220° C. But more precise measurement of these distant temperatures reveals new facts about the planets—such as surface dustiness.

One of the most sensitive of the thermometers for the planets is a germanium bolometer, developed by Dr. Frank Low of the University of Arizona, in the United States. At its heart is a tiny crystal, which responds to slight temperature variations with changes in electrical resistance. Dr. Low's bolometer has found that Jupiter's temperature above the clouds ranges from −125° to −143° C. Cold as that may seem, it was higher than expected, suggesting to him that Jupiter emits heat of its own.

Deep Dishes and Tandem Detectors

Among the most valuable sources of information about the planets are the radio waves they emit. From the intensity of the waves it is possible to deduce the temperatures of planetary atmospheres, and from the length of the waves the depth within the atmospheres of radio sources. Most important, radio waves bring data that visible light does not—clues to magnetic fields, for instance.

The telescopes used for observing these waves are not telescopes in the usual sense, but extremely delicate radio receivers with huge antennae:

the world's largest (*below*), on the Caribbean island of Puerto Rico, covers 18½ acres. Enormous dish antennae like this are the best devices for picking up weak radio signals, but more accurate mapping of signal sources is possible with a pair of antennae (*opposite*). A radio telescope can also "feel" the planets by bouncing radar signals off them. Often the results are a surprise: radar from Puerto Rico tracked the edges of Mercury as the planet rotated, and proved that, contrary to a long-held belief, it does not always keep the same face to the sun.

A PAIR OF PIN-POINTERS

The radio telescopes at the California Institute of Technology (*right*) work in tandem to distinguish between planetary radio sources. By mapping the origins of radio waves from the regions around Jupiter, this observatory located belts of charged particles surrounding the planet.

COLOSSUS IN THE VALLEY

Puerto Rico's dish (*below*) is a reflector, focusing natural radio signals from space on to a detector in the carriage suspended from the towers. When the telescope serves as radar, a man-made wave is sent from carriage to dish to planet, then bounced back to dish and carriage.

A TROUGH FOR DISTANT SIGNALS

The huge trough of the University of Illinois radio telescope (*above*) dwarfs four men standing in its centre. Equal in size to more than five football fields, the trough can detect weak radio signals from far out in space. It has received faint signals from beyond our galaxy, the Milky Way, and has also studied radio wave lengths within the solar system from the planet Jupiter.

Tracking Whispers from a Venus Flight

The age of the rocket marked a major turning point in the science of astronomy. Since the early 1960's far-ranging space vehicles have been sending back a wealth of radio data from the reaches of space. But the transmitters are so small and the distances so vast that the signals received on earth are very weak. Collecting them calls for an elaborate base like this one in California, known as the Deep Space Instrumentation Facility of the Jet Propulsion Laboratory. These big radio telescopes relay their signals to a computer; together, the two instruments pick up the faint radio whispers, record the information in their complex variations, diagnose ailing instruments and transmit commands out to the space vehicles.

The signal received from space is

a "carrier beam" that has been made to change in a number of ways so that it can convey many different items of information—almost as if it were a clothes-line carrying assorted items from the family laundry. The carrier may include signals that indicate the speed, course and position of the space vehicles, a burned-out battery or a stuck switch, plus data from several kinds of instruments.

The Goldstone station is the only one of its kind in the United States. It has two 85-foot radio telescopes and a 210-foot dish, so powerful that it can track flights to Pluto, 3,580 million miles away. Four similar stations located in Canberra and Woomera, Australia, Johannesburg, South Africa, and Madrid, Spain, work with Goldstone to keep constant contact with U.S. deep-space probes.

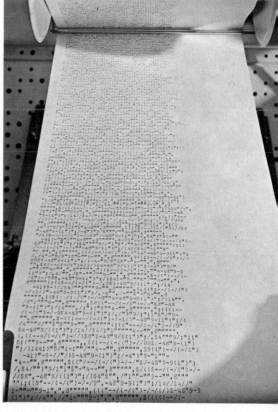

A MESSAGE FROM MARINER
A coded message from Mariner II comes out of a teleprinter. The code is in the form of letters and symbols, which the computer translates into physical measurements. If a symbol is repeated for an entire line on the print sheet, it indicates that an instrument is out of order either within the space craft or on the ground.

MONITORING SIGNALS FROM SPACE
Engineers at the Goldstone tracking station listen to signals from the Venus-bound space craft Mariner II as they are picked up by the radio telescope outside. Almost immediately a computer begins to convert the signals to a number code that indicates how well Mariner is working.

A BALLOON'S DELICATE CARGO
A motor-steered telescope and a spectroscope (*above*) are the main instruments that were carried into space by a Johns Hopkins University balloon to measure infra-red radiation reflected by the clouds and upper atmosphere of Venus.

GASSING UP FOR A HIGH RIDE
A balloon takes in lighter-than-air helium at Holloman Air Force Base in New Mexico before being launched by a special lorry (*right*). The balloon material, made of plastic only 2/1,000 inch thick, can lift a one-ton astronomical instrument package to an altitude of almost 90,000 feet. At that level the atmosphere is so thin that the balloon, which is almost collapsed at launching, expands to a diameter of 202 feet.

A Balloon's-Eye View of Planets

The earth's own atmosphere is the chief obstacle to a clear view of the heavens. The reason stars twinkle and the images of planets shimmer is that the air swirls and roils like a stormy sea. Astronomers have tried to escape this interference by building observatories on mountain-tops, above most of the turbulence and clouds. Even up there, absorption of light by ozone, carbon dioxide and water in the atmosphere blocks the scientists' observation of most infrared and ultra-violet radiation.

Only when the first automatically guided telescopes were sent aloft on balloons in 1959 were these limitations of the atmosphere partly overcome. By means of balloons, thousands of pounds of instruments at a time could be raised almost entirely beyond the atmosphere. Guided by devices that automatically sighted on stars or the sun, the balloon-borne telescopes have tracked Mars, Venus and Jupiter, giving scientists some of the most unusual analyses they have ever had of planetary atmospheres.

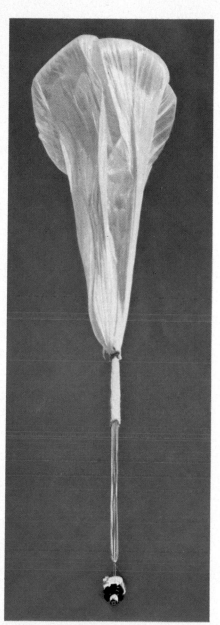

TOWARDS THE ATMOSPHERE'S LIMIT
The balloon-borne instrument package of the Johns Hopkins Venus project rises into the sky. This balloon reached an altitude of 16½ miles; free of most of the atmosphere's absorption, it detected water vapour near Venus's clouds.

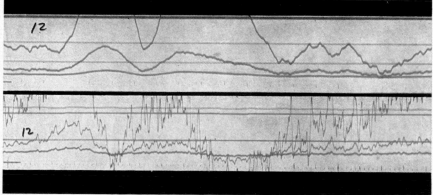

EVIDENCE OF ICE FROM VENUS
The wavy lines on the graph above contained an important clue for astronomers. Obtained during a 1964 balloon flight, the lines reflect the intensity of specific infra-red waves—evidence for ice crystals in Venus's cloud deck. Venera probes later detected water vapour below the clouds. Since water blocks heat loss, these findings help to explain why Venus is so hot.

Pre-Flight Check for a Mars Mission

LNO	171	172	173	174	175	176
100	35	36	36	36	36	37
101	33	34	34	33	34	34
102	33	34	34	33	34	33
103	33	33	33	33	33	33
104	33	34	33	34	33	33
105	33	34	34	33	34	34
106	33	34	34	34	34	34
107	33	33	33	34	35	34
108	33	34	34	34	34	34
109	34	33	34	34	34	34
110	33	34	33	34	33	33
111	33	34	34	34	34	33
112	33	34	35	34	34	34
113	33	34	35	34	35	34
114	33	34	35	34	35	34
115	32	34	33	34	34	34
116	33	34	33	34	34	34
117	33	33	34	33	34	34
118	32	33	34	34	35	34
119	33	33	35	34	35	34

A PICTURE BY NUMBERS
Mariner IV flashed back a series of numbers, each representing the intensity of spots of light on a television screen. When the numbers were translated, a picture of a part of Mars emerged.

The pitted regions of Mars, the blazing deserts of Venus, the dusty surface of the moon—such explicit details were confirmed only by sending complex instruments far from earth to examine the planets at close range.

Among the most ambitious of these probes was that of Mariner IV, some of whose equipment is shown here. First in a series of space craft that reconnoitred Mars, this vehicle, sent off in 1964, consisted of 575 pounds of rocket-propelled laboratory. After it streaked through space for seven and a half months, it passed within 6,118 miles of Mars. Fastened to Mariner's chassis of magnesium and aluminium alloy were 31,696 electronic components. During the long journey, these instruments detected solar protons, recorded interplanetary dust, transmitted radio signals back to earth through the Martian atmosphere and determined its density, searched for a weak magnetic field around the planet, sent close-up television pictures of the Martian surface back to earth, and captured photographic evidence of craters on the planet's surface.

Astronomers immediately began to plan for the day when a far more complex craft, Viking, is intended to approach Mars, send exploratory capsules down to the very surface of the planet and relay their findings back.

MARINER IV'S TELESCOPIC EYES
The photographic equipment carried by Mariner IV consisted of a telescope and television camera (top tube) and two sensors (bottom tubes) that aimed the camera. Pictures were taken at distances ranging from 10,430 to 8,160 miles away. The total of 22 photographs, covering a 6,200-mile strip (*pages 144, 145*), showed about 1 per cent of the planet's surface.

A HEAT TEST FOR MARINER IV
In a test chamber, technicians check the temperature of the surfaces of Mariner IV. Overhead lamps flooded the craft with the same intensity of ultra-violet and other light waves it would experience in space, thus determining how its parts would stand up to radiation during its trip.

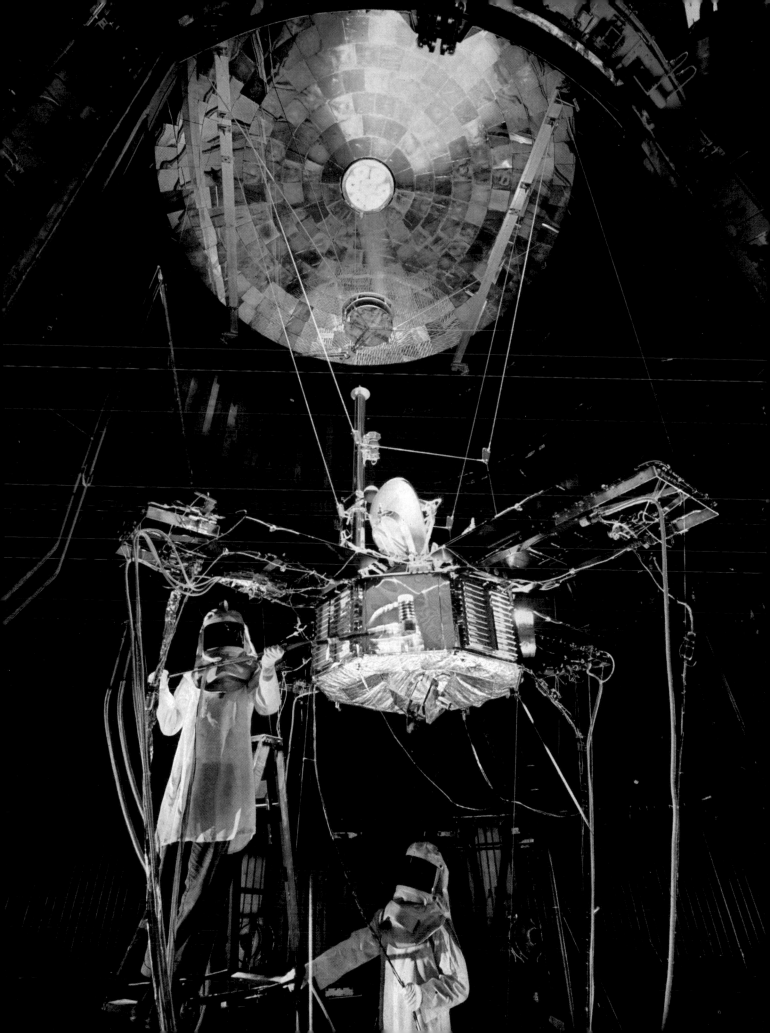

4
The Lessons
of
the Moon

Compiling the first comprehensive geologic moon map, lunar geologist Eugene Shoemaker checks detail maps on the wall and floor.

THE EARTH is a minor planet, but its respectably large moon gives it a major distinction. While all other planets far outrank their satellites or have none, the earth and moon are so close in size that they can be called a double planet. Viewed from Venus or Mars they must be a fascinating sight: a small planet chasing a bigger one across the sky, sometimes ahead of it, sometimes behind, and on rare occasions crossing its face, casting a shadow on it or disappearing behind it. If Mars ever had astrologers, they must have used this stately dance for predicting the future, and the motions of the earth and moon about each other could well have taught Martian astronomers the principles of gravitation.

To human observers the moon is one of the most rewarding objects in the sky. It is so close—less than one-hundredth of the distance to Venus —that even the unaided eye sees fascinating markings on it. For centuries astronomers studied it with telescopes and long before the era of space flight they theorized about what it would be like to stand on its surface. The moon's sky, they knew, would always be black, even in daytime. The blue of the earth's sky is a consequence of the atmosphere; the moon has none. The earth, from those locales on the moon where it is visible, would always hang in the same part of the lunar sky. It would show phases like the moon's and would rotate entertainingly. Its diameter would always appear about four times as great as the moon's does from the earth, but because of its greater reflectivity it would give about 80 times as much light. Even a crescent earth would be bright enough to read by, and the cold blue light of the full earth falling on the moon would be sufficient for many kinds of work.

Even among the lunar mountains the scenery was long known to be dull. Although the peaks are often quite high, most slopes on the moon are rarely steeper than 15 degrees. Peaks are broad-based and rounded on top. (The moon's reputation for ruggedness comes chiefly from photographs taken in low-angle sunlight, when the shadows cast by the shallow, sloping topography are long and conspicuous). This gentle relief is not surprising in view of the moon's airless condition. If the earth had no atmosphere, water, wind or ice to carve its features, its surface would probably be just as dull as the moon's and, as we shall see, it would also be pocked by craters.

Man's first landing on the moon on July 20, 1969, was the triumphant climax of an age-old fascination. As long ago as ancient Greece, when the planets were known merely as points of light, the moon was recognized as a sphere and its changing shape was correctly attributed to sunlight falling on it from varying directions. The time between new moons was measured with fair accuracy, and the fact that the same face is always turned towards the earth with only minor wobblings was noted although not explained. (The modern explanation is, in part, that the moon is not a perfectly symmetrical spheroid. It has a massive bulge which the earth's gravitation attracts like a plumb bob, thus keeping the same hemisphere pointing towards the earth.)

Not much more was learned about the moon until the 17th century, when the telescope first brought its mountains and circular craters into view. Its dark, smooth-looking areas were thought to be seas and were named accordingly: the Sea of Clouds, the Sea of Rains, etc. Recently, new techniques of observation and analysis have shown that the long-studied moon is packed with perplexing mysteries. Many of its features are far from being explained, though its blotched and pitted face is recognized to be an ancient inscription recording events that happened in the solar system thousands of millions of years ago.

Airless surface

The actual origin of the moon is a much-debated matter. Some experts hold that it was formed at the same time as the earth and has been its satellite from the beginning. Others think it was once part of the earth. Still others argue that it was formed at a different time and place out of different material, spent its early youth as an independent planet and was later captured by the earth and reduced to the rank of satellite.

The moon's diameter is about 2,160 miles, roughly one-quarter that of the earth, but its mass is only $^1/_{81}$ of the earth's. This comparatively low mass and the lunar radius have been critical in the moon's evolution. They have made the gravitational pull at its surface one-sixth that of the earth, so objects on it can escape into space more easily. The escape velocity is about 1.5 miles per second. To escape from the earth an object must travel almost 7 miles per second.

The ease of escape applies not only to space craft bringing astronauts home from the moon but also to gases near the moon's surface. Most gas molecules present there, accelerated by the temperatures prevailing during the moon's long, sunlit day, would get moving fast enough to soar into space and never come back. Thus, if the moon had an atmosphere early in its history, the gases would long since have escaped. Any additional gas molecules that might have been emitted from its interior over the years would be lost in the same way.

Astronomers have made manful attempts to detect some sort of atmosphere on the moon but the most delicate tests show at most an extremely diffuse halo of electrically charged particles. The density of this ghost of an atmosphere is around one-tenth of a million-millionth of the earth's. For most purposes the lunar atmosphere might as well not exist. Neither can liquid water exist for long on the moon's surface. It must either freeze in some sheltered cranny or evaporate and escape.

With no appreciable atmosphere to shield it, the moon is unprotected against the violence of space. Solar radiation strikes it at full strength with its X-rays and ultra-violet light. In addition, charged particles from the sun—the so-called "solar wind"—hit the surface, as do low-energy cosmic rays and micrometeorites, those minute specks of dust moving at cosmic speeds. All these varied assailants have been searing the moon's surface for thousands of millions of years, while the earth is so well sheltered by its atmosphere and its magnetic field that the very existence of most of these attackers was not suspected until rather recently.

GALILEO'S MOON, one of the first drawings made from telescopic observations, around 1610, has a rough, mountainous surface. Noticing the ragged demarcation line between the dark and light sides of the moon, Galileo concluded, rightly, that the irregularity was caused by high mountains and shadowed valley. But he erred in suggesting that this topography closely resembled the earth's.

As if in recompense, the moon is immune to another kind of attack. Its airless, waterless surface is not subjected to the powerful wind and water erosion that gnaws the earth's mountains down to their roots in a few hundred million years, nor has the moon experienced the internal movements that are still wrinkling the crust of the earth. Long, parallel mountain ridges, the earth's boldest features, are largely absent.

While the moon lacks the familiar features of the earth, it has others that do not resemble the earth's and cannot be accounted for in familiar earthly terms. There are the wide, dark "seas", or *maria*; the great, ring-shaped craters, which superficially suggest volcanoes but are as much as 150 miles in diameter; and the long, bright rays radiating from some of the craters. What is the nature of all these curious things, so different from earthly topography? There is still disagreement about some of them and hardly any knowledge about a few, but modern selenology, the science of the moon's physical features, has progressed enough to tell with a good deal of confidence how the moon's face reached its present interesting condition.

Impact Craters

The most striking and unusual features on the moon are the gigantic craters that cover much of the surface. In the early years of selenology they were thought to be volcanic, but modern evidence indicates they were excavated by objects impacting the moon from space. Some of the objects were small meteorites like those that frequently hit the earth; others were many miles in diameter, big enough to be classed as asteroids, or small planets, like those that follow orbits between Mars and Jupiter. Still others were probably the nuclei of comets. Whatever their size or nature, they hit with enormous speed and the explosive effect of their impacts blasted craters much larger than themselves.

There is little doubt that meteorite impacts were the most important force in shaping the surface of the moon during most of its history. Their concentrated work can be seen in the bright-appearing "highlands", located mostly in the moon's southern hemisphere, where craters are so crowded that they overlap. These highlands are believed to be the oldest areas on the moon, dating from the youth of the solar system. During this period interplanetary space swarmed with wandering objects of all sizes. In rapid succession they rained on the young moon, building it larger and larger and blasting craters that were soon erased by later impacts. The formative period may have continued only a few hundred million years, until the moon (or the earth-moon system) attracted the smaller bodies and swept its orbit almost clear. Then came comparative quiet. Since the moon has no wind or water erosion, the ancient formations have lasted more than 4,000 million years with only minor changes and are still exposed to view.

The rest of the moon, with its level maria, fresher craters and easily seen domes and rills, is not at all like the jumbled, ancient highlands. Its structures are simpler and more isolated and they are interrelated in

THE MOON'S SURFACE is depicted in these two 17th-century drawings. The illustration above, by Francesco Fontana, was one of the first to include the moon's rays, pin-wheels of powdery material splashed out by meteorites as they crashed and formed craters. The drawing below, by Johannes Hevelius, shows the 59 per cent of the moon visible from earth.

ways that enable experts to determine their comparative ages confidently.

The simplest example of this dating system is the easy proof that the craters known as Tycho and Copernicus are among the youngest major structures on the moon. Each is surrounded by rays streaking outwards like the petals of a scraggy flower. The rays overlie everything in their paths, climbing the rims of other craters, marching across maria and mountains. The fact that they are superimposed on other features is proof that they are younger.

A collision at 50 miles per second

The rays of a crater are believed to consist of finely powdered lunar surface material shot out in long jets by meteorite impact. It is not hard to reconstruct, roughly at least, what happens when a denizen of interplanetary space crashes into the moon. Its speed may be as great as 50 miles per second, but even five miles per second gives it many times the energy of an equal quantity of exploding TNT. It penetrates a little way below the surface and turns into a mass of hot, highly compressed gas that expands irresistibly, sends out a shattering shock wave and tosses debris far and wide. Great blocks of moon rock pile up on the crater rim and incandescent jets of fast-moving dust and rock fragments shoot out in all directions. Those that soar sharply upwards fall back to form the bright halos outside the rims while those that shoot outwards travel great distances to form the long rays. Both halos and rays are peppered with secondary craters where heavy pieces of ejected material strike the surface and dig holes of their own.

It is likely that all the large craters on the moon, including the most ancient ones, were typical ray craters when they were first made, but with the slow passage of millions or thousands of millions of years they grew dim and obscure. Later impacts tossed dirt and debris over them or blasted gaps in their rims. A gradual darkening process that affects the entire lunar surface erased their bright rays and halos.

After the early formative period of the moon's youth, so goes the best-established theory, the cratering process continued at a slower pace. Small meteorites dug their small craters and every few million years or so a more violent impact blasted a crater that looked at first much as Copernicus does now.

Then came the biggest of all. A massive body, perhaps an asteroid 100 miles in diameter, crashed into the moon north of centre of the present Mare Imbrium. The exact place where it hit is the point of intersection of the many radial valleys gouged by high-speed missiles from the great ensuing explosion. The Imbrian Event, as lunar experts call it, did much more than blast a crater. It must have shaken the entire moon and cracked its exterior.

THE SEA OF RAINS, or Mare Imbrium, shown in the square above, was given a name suggesting a lunar ocean. But astronomers have long known that no surface water exists on the moon. Such "seas" are believed to be huge, ancient craters filled with lava and meteoritic dust. The drawings on the right show how the Mare Imbrium region might have been created. First the moon absorbs the impact of a giant meteorite or planetoid. The raised rim of the crater, the rough terrain around it and the light streaks radiating from it were all created by the force of the tremendous impact. Over a period of time (*second drawing*) a number of smaller meteorites crash into the moon's surface, one of them causing the crater's periphery to slump, forming an enlarged basin. The rays of the first crater are obscured by erosion, but those of the newer craters are clearly visible. The third drawing shows the lunar sea with the basin filled and only a few rayed craters remaining. Finally there is the Mare Imbrium area as it is seen today, with all the rays darkened by erosion.

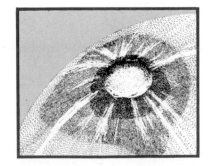

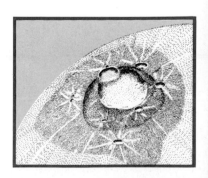

Striking proof of the Imbrian Event's enormous effect are the circular rings of mountains, some of them 20,000 feet high, that surround the impact point. These rings are more than 1,000 miles in diameter and are believed to have been formed by shock waves that travelled through the moon rock and froze in the places where they are seen today. A rough terrestrial equivalent of the Imbrian Event would be an explosion that dug the Gulf of Mexico and raised most of the Rocky Mountains in the same few awesome minutes.

When freshly blasted, the Imbrium crater may have been more than 100 miles deep but, before long, material rising from below partially filled it while the steep sides slumped towards the centre. Even in this collapsed condition it must have been the moon's most conspicuous feature, a vast pit nearly 500 miles in diameter walled by a circular rim higher than any earthly mountains.

It is natural to ask why the moon should have suffered so many blows from space while the earth, probably its close companion for several thousand million years, seems to have escaped. The answer is that the earth did not escape; it merely covered most of its scars. As soon as scientists began to search seriously for impact craters on the earth they found plenty of them. The famous Canyon Diablo crater in Arizona is only the most obvious and best preserved. Maps and aerial photographs have led searchers to many other intriguing circular formations. In Canada several large, almost perfectly circular lakes have been identified. Their features can be explained only as the result of meteorite impacts. Similar structures exist in many other parts of the earth.

The great scars left by meteorites

Drilling shows that these "astroblemes" (star-scars) usually contain the broken rubble that is to be expected in a meteorite crater. They are often surrounded by bedrock full of cone-shaped fractures made by the shock wave. There is seldom any trace of the meteorite itself, but this is not surprising. Unless it hits at unusually low speed, a meteorite will vaporize and spurt out of the crater as gas.

The biggest structure on earth that is suspected of being part of an astrobleme is near the Nastopoka Island chain on the eastern shore of Hudson Bay. These islands form a beautifully circular arc with its centre of curvature, where a great meteor may have hit, out in the bay itself. If they are segments of an ancient rim, the crater must have been 275 miles in diameter, bigger than all but a very few craters on the moon. Not far away, the curving shores of the Gulf of St. Lawrence outline a somewhat smaller circle.

After the Imbrian Event the next stage in the moon's evolution was the development of the maria, the great level plains that are the moon's

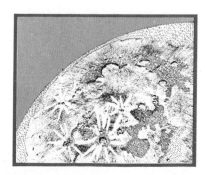
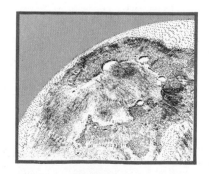

most conspicuous feature. This time the changes were caused by influence from within the moon, rather than from surrounding space.

The maria are widely believed to be fields of lava that flowed through the surface and were later pulverized by micrometeorites, although the origin of the lava is still in doubt. Like the earth, the moon is thought to have originally formed as a fairly cool, solid body, and it apparently stayed solid long after radioactivity had heated the earth and melted much of its interior. Some experts believe that most of the moon's interior never got hot enough to soften but that parts near the surface did. One conjecture is that large impacts such as the Imbrian Event filled the brittle moon with fractures. When zones of the interior were melted by radioactivity and the heat produced by meteorite impacts, the lava that was formed came to the surface through the cracks. It may have flooded out at different times, filling low areas such as Oceanus Procellarum and turning the Imbrian depression into Mare Imbrium. Ridges were no barrier for the lava, which moved underground as well as on the surface. In this way it could have penetrated many craters, turning the larger ones into flat, circular plains such as Mare Crisium and Mare Nectaris. Inside some craters, such as Wargentin, pressure seems to have forced the lava to high levels, above the level of the surface outside the craters.

Water and dust floods

Not all experts accepted the lava theory. A minority insisted that the moon had always been solid inside and that some other explanation must be found for the maria. One suggestion was that large amounts of water or some other fluid gushed out of the moon, carried suspended material into low places and then evaporated. Another hypothesized great clouds of gassy dust, like terrestrial volcanic ash-flows, that deposited dry material in the low places. Still another proposal involves fine dust, eroded off lunar rocks by micrometeorites and possibly buoyed slightly above the surface by electrostatic forces. This might flow downhill like a thin liquid, fill low areas and turn them into level maria.

Whatever the mare material may be, it soon became solid, conforming with remarkable accuracy to the moon's general shape. The period of mare formation is loosely set at 3,000 million years ago and it did not continue for long. After it was over the moon resumed its routine existence, steadily pitted by small meteorites and occasionally shaken to its centre by a big one, but none big enough to produce another Mare Imbrium.

Although the principal evidence for volcanism on the moon is basalt-like material that fills the maria, there are other signs of it too. Scattered irregularly over the lunar surface are small, low-rimmed craters surrounded by very dark halos. They are probably vents through which gases carried material from the moon's interior that blackened the near-by surface. There are also small craters arranged in rows and these too are believed to be volcanic. They presumably trace a crack that released high-pressure gas deep in the moon's interior.

One of the most stubborn riddles presented by the moon is its surface

THE CANYON DIABLO CRATER in Arizona, three-quarters of a mile wide, was the first on earth to be positively identified as an astrobleme—a scar left by a giant meteorite. The clinching evidence was the discovery in 1960 that the crater contained coesite, a form of silica created by millions of pounds of force. Only the impact of a large object, believed to be a meteorite that landed about 25,000 years ago, could have produced such force.

structure and composition. For one thing, the lunar surface is surprisingly dark in colour. The moon looks bright when it floats majestically across a clear night sky, but only because it has no competition. Actually its maria are about as dark as freshly washed blackboards. Other parts of the moon are somewhat lighter, but even the brightest rays and highlands might look as dark as black roads if they were brought to the earth. As astronomers put it, the full moon's "visual albedo" is 0.073, which means that it reflects only 7.3 per cent of the visible light that hits it. By comparison, the earth is five times as reflective, cloud-covered Venus ten times as reflective.

The appearance of the lunar surface also changes in a peculiar way: its brightness increases sharply when sunlight falls on it from the direction of the observer. The full moon, which is seen when the sun is almost behind the earth, is not merely twice as bright as the half-moon. It is nine times as bright, and the light reflected from it doubles during the last two days before it is full.

The only kind of surface that would behave this way is one that is riddled with cavities. The cavities show as black shadows when sunlit from one side but disappear when sunlight comes from the observer's direction to illuminate their bottoms. No common powder or granulated substance gives quite this effect. The natural material that most closely approaches the moon's reflecting properties is *Cladonia rangiferina*, a spongy lichen with many fine clefts, but no one thinks the moon is a field of lichen.

A fresh crop of mysteries

Some of these puzzles were cleared up, at least in part, when U.S. and Soviet space craft began to approach the moon, orbit around it, land on it to send back television pictures and at last, in 1969, to set on its hostile surface astronauts who returned with lunar samples. But many old problems still went unsolved. Indeed, the new ways of observing the moon revealed fresh mysteries to be explained.

Pictures taken by U.S. Lunar Orbiter space craft circling the moon show what look uncannily like meandering river channels. They may have carried water that evaporated millions of years ago. On the other hand, they may have been made by some other flowing substance such as lava or dust mixed with gas, or they may be the collapsed roofs of underground channels where one of these fluids once flowed. The solution of this puzzle may have to await the arrival of scientists on the banks of the mysterious "river channels".

The Orbiters also revealed curious features of the moon that have no analogy on the earth. As they circled, their courses varied slightly in unexpected ways. Analysis showed that these wanderings were due to local variations in the moon's gravitational field. Over most of the moon's "seas" the gravitational force on the Orbiters is slightly stronger. Seven or eight of these "mascons"—a word coined from "mass concentration"—are known, and they are being intensively mapped because they affect the behaviour of lunar landing craft. No one is sure what causes them. Masses

ASTROBLEMES in North America, located on the map above, are the scars of meteorite bombardments that have pockmarked the earth and moon over the past four to five thousand million years. The arrow indicates the Canyon Diablo crater (*opposite*). The huge circular formation at the lower end of Hudson Bay, 275 miles in diameter, is the world's largest suspected astrobleme. However, mountain-building and water erosion have obliterated most of the earth's astroblemes, while erosion on the moon has had less effect on lunar craters.

of heavy substances—such as meteoric iron—may be buried below the surface or heavy lava may have flowed into low areas, forming the "seas" and giving them extra-strong gravitational pull.

The spectacular pictures taken by space craft and the astronauts themselves showed many new details on the moon's surface. Some of them were expected, such as impact craters of all sizes down to a small fraction of an inch in diameter. Presumably the moon has thousands of millions of these miniature craters blasted by micrometeorites. Some of the space craft pictures give enlarged views of one of the conspicuous, bright rays from the crater Tycho. As was expected by astronomers, they show small secondary craters dug by sizeable chunks of rock thrown out of Tycho along with the powdery ray material. What was not expected is the relative rareness of loose rocks on the surface surrounding the crater, although other parts of the moon are thickly strewn with rocks. Tycho is a very young crater, so rocks thrown out of it would not have had time to be covered by slowly accumulating dust. Perhaps a better explanation is that the lunar surface is so yielding in places that rocks blasted from the Tycho crater plunged deeply into it and disappeared.

Ranger IX, one of the earliest successful lunar space craft, provided scientists with still another surprise by revealing the slump pits that dot the surface in many places. They are on mare material and they look superficially like small craters. But they cannot be craters because they lack raised rims of ejected debris, and their cross-sections resemble wineglasses rather than the bowl shapes of ordinary impact craters. They seem to have been formed by loose surface material falling or draining into underground cavities. Many places on the earth have similar slump pits where the ground has collapsed into limestone caves that were excavated by running water dissolving the limestone just below the surface.

Caves for an astronaut base

The moon's slump pits suggest that much of the mare material has large, weak-roofed cavities in it. How they got there is not known, but an obvious possibility is that they are gas bubbles in solidified lava, perhaps permitted to grow to great size by the moon's surface vacuum and low gravity. When the bubbly surface was covered with debris from later meteorite impacts, some of the weakest bubbles collapsed under the weight, allowing loose material to sink, leaving slump pits on the surface and releasing puffs of gas into space.

Astronauts moving across the lunar surface will be cautious when approaching such treacherous places, but the caves may prove extremely valuable for sheltering lunar explorers. Even a few feet underground, the caves will be cooler than the surface by day, warmer by night. Large caves with strong walls could perhaps be sealed, filled with breathable gas and used as long-term quarters. There the explorers would be well protected from micrometeorites, solar protons and other inclemencies of the lunar outdoors. Caves on the moon were foreseen by H. G. Wells. His novel *The First Men in the Moon*, published in 1901, is not one of his finest

HOSTILE MOON MEN, shown capturing an explorer from earth in this illustration from H. G. Wells's 1901 novel, *First Men in the Moon*, fascinated early generations of science-fiction readers. Called Selenites, they were intelligent, spindly-limbed creatures who lived in underground lunar caves, breathed oxygen in a rarefied atmosphere and ate fungi. Though such beings seemed plausible when the novel was published, astronomers now realize that, since the moon lacks an atmosphere and surface water, the chances that it supports life are very slim.

works of science fiction and the intelligent "Selenites" he depicted inhabiting the caves are not to be taken seriously. But if earthlings do try to colonize the moon they will certainly search, like the Wellsian Selenites, for caves or crevasses leading below its inhospitable surface.

Colonies on the moon are still a project for the future. But even the first lunar landing provided scientists with abundant material for years of study and argument, particularly over the interpretation of the many kinds of soil and rock samples brought back to earth. The Apollo 11 landing spot, the Sea of Tranquillity, was chosen in advance because of its comparative smoothness. Also, because rays of material ejected from distant impact craters pass near or over it, the area promised to supply the astronauts with moon rocks of widely varying type and origin.

The choice proved excellent. The space craft landed on an almost level surface of fine, dark-grey dust littered thinly with rocks of all sizes up to two and a half feet long. Some of them lay on the surface; others were deeply embedded in the dust, which was powdery on top, much firmer below. Most but not all of the rocks were rounded as if some sort of erosion had nibbled them away.

Igneous moon rocks

Even a superficial examination of these and later rock samples showed that they were different from anything found on earth. Many were igneous; that is, they had solidified from a melted state. Perhaps the moon's surface was hot and liquid once, like the interior of the earth. The source of the heat might have been radioactivity. Analysis of the igneous rocks showed them to contain enough radioactive material, mostly thorium and uranium, to heat them to the melting point over a long period of time. The moon's interior is not believed to be hot and plastic at present, however, and the igneous rocks found by the astronauts can represent only a small part of its total mass. Another possibility is that melting was caused by the heat released by the impact events that produced the craters.

The igneous rocks consist mostly of silicates and roughly resemble basalt, the rock that underlies the earth's oceans and continents, but there are interesting differences. Certain elements, notably titanium, are much more plentiful than they are in the earth's rocks and other elements are less abundant. These differences are so striking that most scientists now believe that the earth and moon could never have been a single body. Those who once believed that the Pacific Ocean was formed when the moon was torn out of the earth's side will have to account for the Pacific in some other way.

The moon's rocks, like many earthly varieties, contain a type of potassium that is radioactive and changes very slowly into argon, so their age can be determined by measuring how much argon the potassium has produced. Many of the igneous rocks brought back by Apollo astronauts were about 3,000 million years old. But there was one rock in the haul from Apollo 12 that was 4,600 million years old, nearly as old as the earth where rocks of this age have long since been destroyed by erosion or melting. It is assumed that this very old rock is a sample of the primitive crust of the moon. Rocks of such age were expected to be plentiful in the lunar highlands, which are geologically older than the lowlands. Yet most of the rocks from Fra Mauro, the highland landing spot of the Apollo 14 mission, were only about 3,900 million years old, indicating that even there the moon's surface has not remained undisturbed since its beginnings.

One of the unusual characteristics of the moon's rocks is their comparative richness in rare elements—including titanium and zirconium—with high melting points, and their poverty in elements, such as sodium and potassium, with low melting points. This difference suggests that the moon was formed in a way that favoured the collection of less fusible elements. Here is a new mystery for scientists to puzzle over.

Erosion from space

Besides igneous rocks, the astronauts brought back breccia: a mixture of rock fragments, grains and dust compressed into a solid mass. This material was presumably made of debris piled up by meteor impacts. There is evidence that later impacts sent shock waves through it and cemented its particles together. Still later impacts scattered them over the plain where the astronauts found them.

Both igneous rocks and breccias are rounded and show other signs of erosion on their exposed surfaces. In many cases the under-surfaces protected by the lunar "soil" look fresh-broken and angular. The breccias look as if they were sand-blasted, with hard, crystalline grains protruding above a worn, softer matrix.

The nature of the erosion process is not fully known. Some of it is undoubtedly the work of micrometeorites—many of the rocks show small circular pits lined with shiny glass where particles moving at tremendous speed hit them and turned small amounts of them into high-temperature gas. Some rocks have these mini-craters on their undersides also, which means that they were turned over at least once in their history, perhaps several times.

Other erosive forces besides meteorites have probably also worked on the rocks. Cosmic rays and the solar wind of particles streaming out of the sun may have caused some of the damage. There is also evidence that the great difference of temperature between the lunar day and night may split off chips of rock. But no one understands fully the slow erosive forces on the airless moon.

The dusty soil that covered most of the Apollo landing sites proved at least as interesting as the rocks. As predicted by theory and partially checked by unmanned Surveyor flights, the surface consists of very fine, nearly black powder whose darkness may be due to concentrations of iron left when the solar wind bombards fine powders and boils off atoms of lighter weight. The powders, first brought back by Apollo 11, have all the properties needed to explain the sometimes puzzling optical properties of the lunar maria. In addition, a special camera for taking three-dimensional close-up pictures of the lunar surface, carried on Apollo missions and taken out onto the moon's surface by the astronauts, revealed shiny patches resembling metalized glass. Glassy spheres are present in fair numbers in lunar dust samples and are probably produced by local melting after a micrometeorite strikes the moon's surface, but the patches found by the 3-D camera seem to exist only in special locales: near the centres of shallow craters and—at least in one case—on a tiny pedestal of dust. To explain such specialized melting it has been suggested that in geologically recent times, perhaps 30,000 years ago, the sun briefly flared to 100 times its usual brightness and melted only those places—crater bottoms and pedestals—which could not cool rapidly.

No trace of life

In spite of elaborate precautions that were taken to avoid all risk of infecting the earth with lunar microbes brought back unintentionally by Apollo 11, no one really expected to find living organisms in the lunar samples. None were found, and none have been found on subsequent missions, although many living earthly organisms, including oysters, germ-free mice and people, were exposed to the moon material. None were infected, and there were no traces of organisms living or dead, or of carbon compounds associated with life. Also absent was any trace of water, including the water that is locked up in the crystals of many of the earth's rocks. There may still be water somewhere on the moon, perhaps as permafrost deep underground. On the evidence presented by the Apollo landings, some scientists have reluctantly concluded that water played little or no part in the evolution of the moon and, without water, life of anything like the earthly type is impossible.

The moon's exploration, however, has hardly begun. Even the samples brought back by Apollo 11 have yet to yield their full stock of information, and they came from one tiny spot on the moon's surface, which is hardly typical. Other landing sites have proved quite different; still others should yield even more information as men gain experience in living and working for long periods on the moon. Already astronauts have learned to operate vehicles on the lunar surface, to study lunar rock formations, to explore lunar craters and to investigate points of unusual interest revealed in photographs—such as the small craters with dark halos that look as if they were made by gases escaping from the moon's interior. Detailed investigation of the lunar subsoil may reveal a layered structure that marks the passage of time like the rings in tree trunks. It may be possible to tell from these how conditions in space have varied since the youth of the moon thousands of millions of years ago. The layers may point, for instance, to periods when dust was unusually plentiful in the solar system, dimming the light of the sun, as has been suggested in theories of the earth's recurrent ice-ages. The chronicle of the lunar soil in favoured places may even reach back to the birth of the solar system. The moon may lack life of its own, but it is not without intense interest for the life—human life—that has just come in contact with it.

RUSSIA'S LUNA IX, the first craft to make a successful soft landing on the moon, is shown in this artist's conception. Only two feet high and weighing 220 pounds, the capsule transmitted a series of remarkable photographs back to earth. Luna IX also dispelled fears that the moon is blanketed by a layer of dust thick enough to engulf exploratory vehicles.

The Earth's Companion

The closest and best-known object in the sky is the earth's constant companion, the moon. This satellite affords many important clues about the nature of the planets. In fact, the moon itself is sometimes referred to as a planet; it differs from true planets only in its orbit, which carries it around the planet Earth, and it probably bears a closer resemblance to certain planets than some planets do to one another. Thus, Mercury and Mars, which have little atmosphere, may be more similar in composition and structure to the airless moon than to the gaseous planets Jupiter and Saturn.

Many facts are known about the moon: its surface (*right*) is a ravaged wasteland; its gravitational pull is so weak that a shell fired from it would travel half-way around its circumference before falling back to the surface; though the moon lights the night on Earth, it actually reflects light poorly. But real investigation of the moon's mysteries has scarcely begun. Only now, when man has set foot on it, will science learn much about the moon's origin, composition and geology. And the first lunar explorations may also provide some of the answers to the nature and origins of the planets.

FEATURES OF THE HALF-MOON
The dark "seas" and the bright craters of the half-moon stand out in sharp contrast in this photograph, which was taken by the 36-inch telescope at the Lick Observatory in California. The crater nearest the centre of the picture is Copernicus, which is as large as Cyprus. The smooth, dark area above Copernicus is one of the moon's largest "seas", Mare Imbrium, the Sea of Rains.

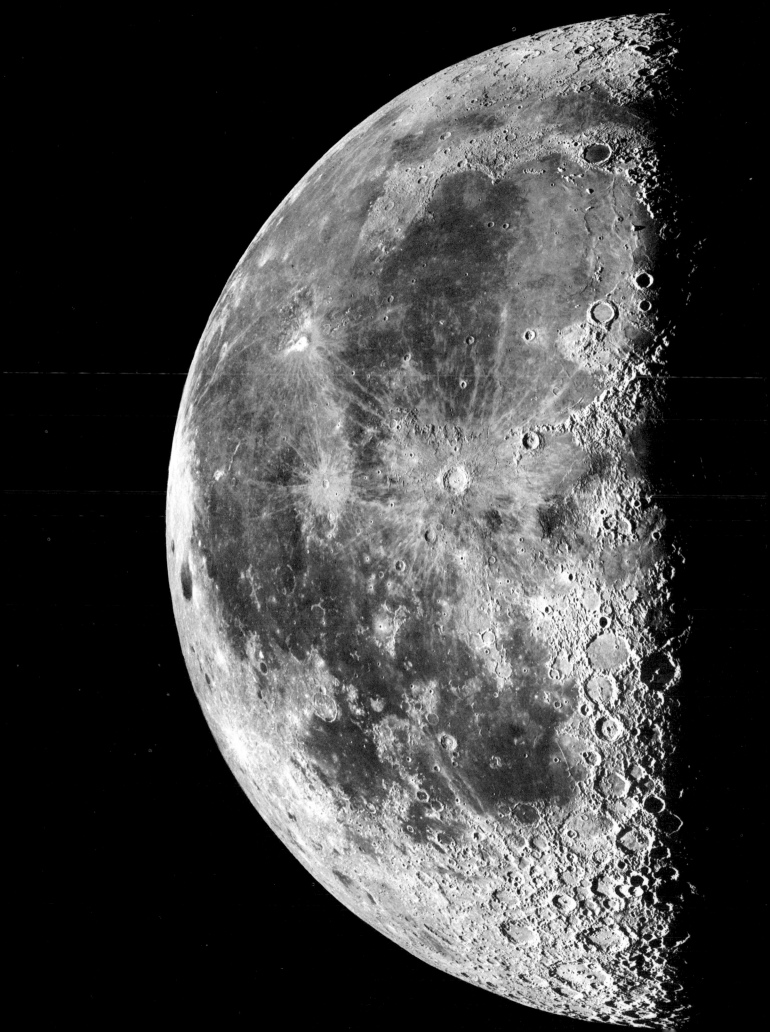

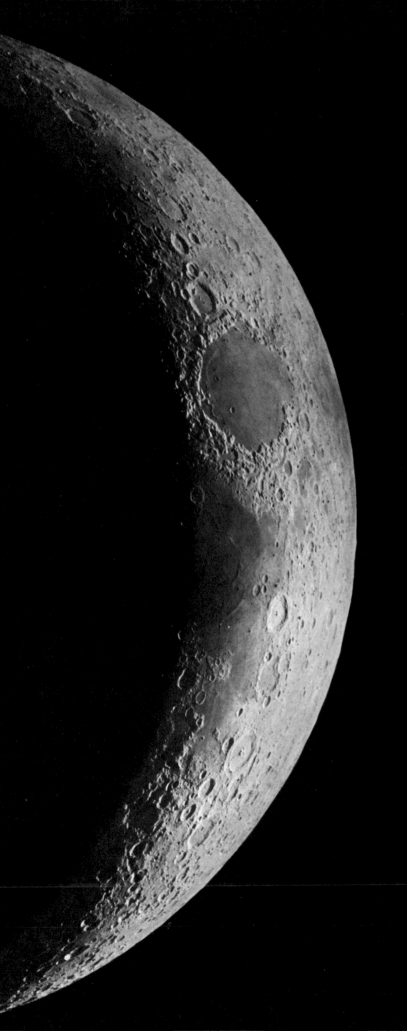

Waterless "Seas" of the Moon

To 17th-century astronomers peering through their telescopes, the dark, smooth areas on the surface of the moon looked like seas, so they called them *maria*, the Latin word for "seas". The term could not have been more inaccurate: the moon has no atmosphere, and consequently no surface water or rain. Maria, which are visible to us as the features of the man in the moon, are now believed to be depressions on the lunar surface that have filled up with lava, meteoritic dust or volcanic ash. They occupy about half the visible surface of the moon; the largest, Oceanus Procellarum, or the Ocean of Storms, where the Soviet space craft Luna IX landed with its instruments in February 1966, covers more than two million square miles, the area of the Caribbean and the Mediterranean Seas together.

Maria are smooth only by comparison with the rest of the moon's areas. Land-swells rise from their surfaces, and small craters and twisted ridges are common within their confines. The maria are probably not unique to the moon; although nothing exactly like them has been observed elsewhere, Mercury and Jupiter's large moons show intriguing spots that may be the first known planetary "seas".

THE CRESCENT'S BLACK EYE
The dull, dark circle of Mare Crisium, the Sea of Crises, stands out like the great eye of a Cyclops in a four-day crescent moon. Deepest of the moon's maria, Mare Crisium is as large as all the Great Lakes, and is readily visible to the naked eye. Its circular shape (distorted here by perspective) as well as the mountains that surround its shores and its dark surface are characteristic features of the maria of the moon.

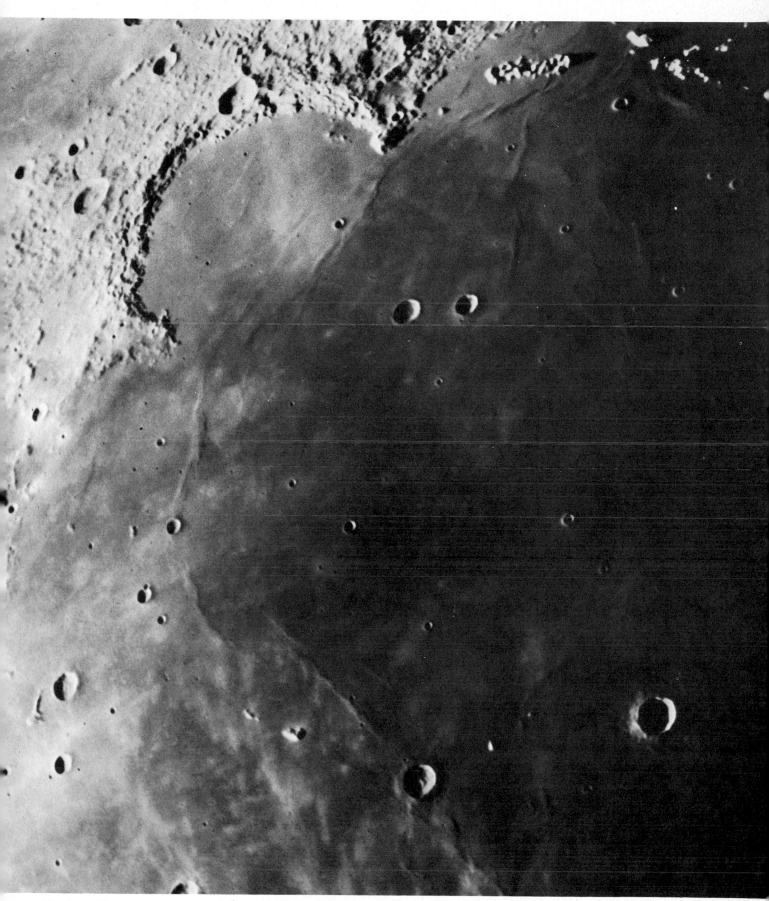

The floor of Mare Imbrium, a lustreless lunar sea some 750 miles wide, is pocked with craterlets, probably caused by meteorites.

The Vast Pits of a Lunar Panorama

The moon is a battered, forbidding place. Its surface is pocked with millions of craters formed by meteoritic bombardment. The earth has been subjected to similar attack but no longer bears witness because wind and water erosion have all but removed the marks. On the moon they stand out stark and desolate. Many craters have high rims and some have terraces or central peaks soaring as high as 7,000 feet. By looking for such features and gauging how much they have been worn down, lunar geologists can gain many valuable insights —they can estimate the age of a pit, decide what caused it to appear and even deduce what other forces later altered it. But the most striking characteristic of the craters is their size. Some are dimples less than an inch in diameter, while others are stupendous pits like Copernicus (*right*) and the gigantic Bailly, which measures 183 miles from rim to rim. The larger craters are actually so big and the curvature of the moon's surface is so great that, if an astronaut were to land in the centre of a large crater, its ramparts would be beyond his horizon.

A SHARP YOUNG CRATER
Glaring sunlight and pitch-black shadows reveal the sharply cut features of the crater Schmidt in this picture taken by the astronauts of Apollo 10. Schmidt, situated on the lunar highlands between the Sea of Tranquillity and Central Bay, is only seven miles across but is one of the newest craters of its size, its rim scarcely eroded and its walls worn by only a few small landslides.

A METEOR'S GIANT HOLE
A breathtaking view of the 60-mile floor and 3,000-foot cliffs of the crater Copernicus was sent from the space craft Lunar Orbiter II in 1966. Copernicus, twice the depth of the Grand Canyon, is a spectacular hole with a mountain range some 2,000 feet high and 10 miles long. It was created when a gigantic meteorite or comet hit the moon less than 10 million years ago.

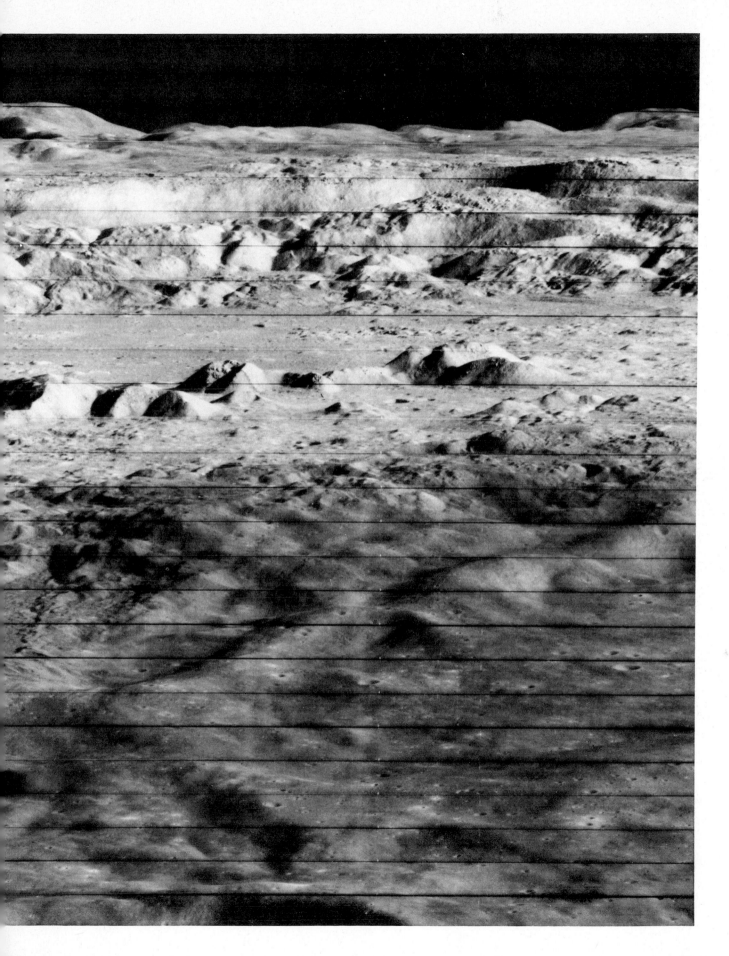

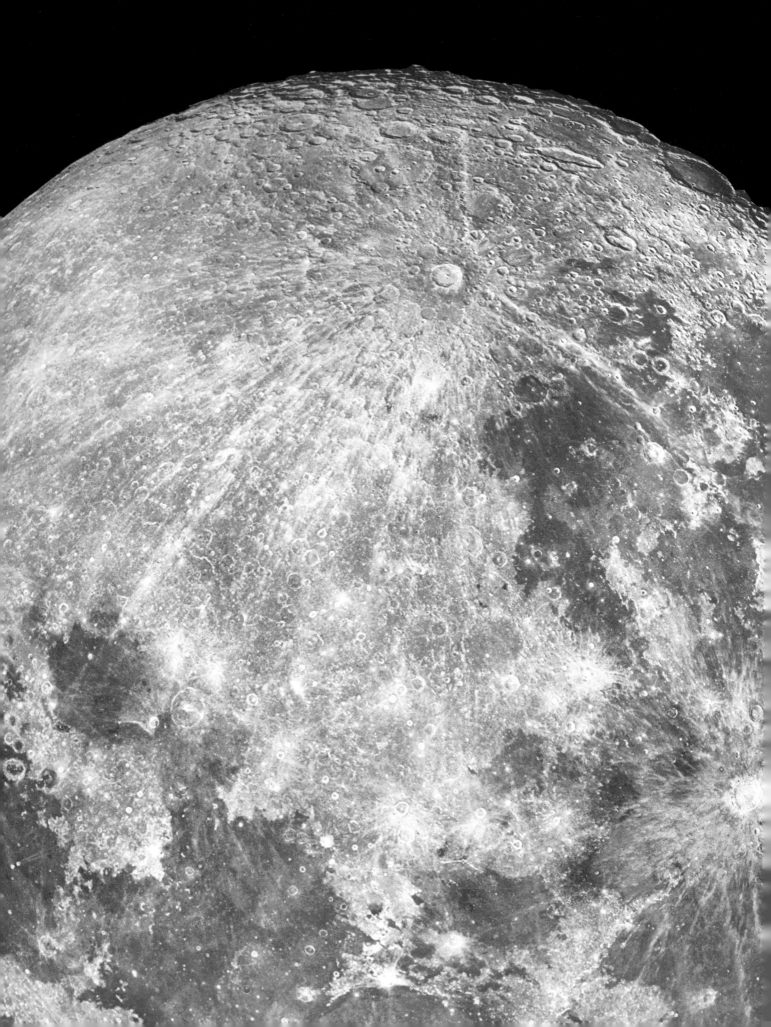

Rills, Rays and a Great Wall

The riotous hotchpotch of the surface of the moon includes many features unlike anything observed on earth: among these are the moon's distinctive rills, or clefts, a great wall formed by the fracturing of the lunar surface, and a series of dazzling rays.

The rays are evident only when the moon is full; at such times, long white streaks are visible radiating from many of the lunar craters. Some rays are as long as 1,500 miles, crossing over mountains, seas and craters.

Astronomers have long debated the nature of these rays. In past years some scientists suggested that they were fields of ice crystals, or salt deposits dried to white intensity by the heat of the sun. Today they are believed to be powdered surface material splattered out of young lunar craters by the meteorites that dug them millions of years ago. Eventually protons, or charged particles from the sun, will darken them into obscurity, like the older rayless craters.

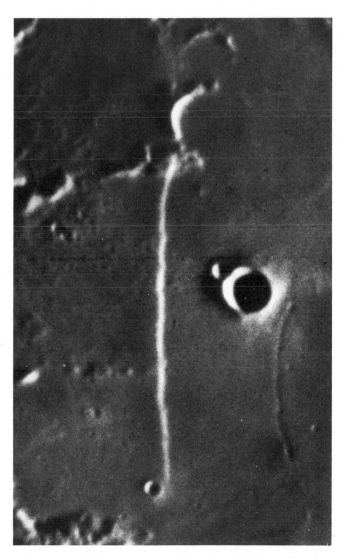

A SINUOUS RILL
Like a moon river flowing into a moon sea, a sinuous rill snakes through the 75-mile-long Alpine Valley towards the Sea of Rains. Findings of Apollo 15 suggest that such rills were formed by lava flowing downhill.

A NETWORK OF RAYS
The most brilliant and extensive system of rays on the moon centres around the crater Tycho. Because this ray network lies on top of other lunar features and has not been disturbed, it is believed to be a relatively new moon feature.

A HUGE CLIFF
The Straight Wall, the only feature of its kind on the moonscape, is a cliff-like mass forced above the lunar surface by internal pressure. Most slopes on the moon are gradual, but this 1,000-foot wall has a 41° slope.

Close Looks at the Lunar Surface

Not until 1959, when the Soviet Lunik III flew around the moon taking pictures, had anyone even glimpsed the moon's far side. But since then a succession of robot and manned space craft has provided close-up views of the lunar surface—between 1964 and 1968 the U.S. sent more than a dozen Ranger, Surveyor and Lunar Orbiter probes to the moon. The information they sent back showed in ever greater detail how strange the moon really is. The first pictures of the far side have now been supplemented by others, revealing, inexplicably, that this hidden face is more pockmarked than the side turned to earth. And views of the near side show clearly such bizarre features as a gigantic rolling stone (*left*), volcanic domes (*below*) and huge mountain ranges circling one of the moon's largest craters (*right*).

A BOULDER THAT MOVED

A sign of action in the eerily dead world of the moon was caught in this picture of a boulder, large as a house, that has rolled 900 feet down a crater slope. Such rolling stones are probably set in motion by quakes or the shocks of meteorite impacts. The fact that the sharp-angled boulder left such a definite track suggests that the surface of the moon here is relatively soft.

MYSTERY DOMES AND MOUNTAINS

Strange straggling lines of hills, odd domes (*above*) and a dramatic bull's-eye of concentric mountain rings (*right*) were revealed by Lunar Orbiter space craft. The domes, ten miles across and 1,500 feet high, seem to be relics of volcanic activity near crater Marius (*below, right edge of horizon*). The concentric ranges encircle Mare Orientale, almost as large as Sweden and Norway combined, and the mountains are correspondingly massive. The Cordillera Mountains, outermost of the three, are 20,000 feet high—much higher than Mont Blanc.

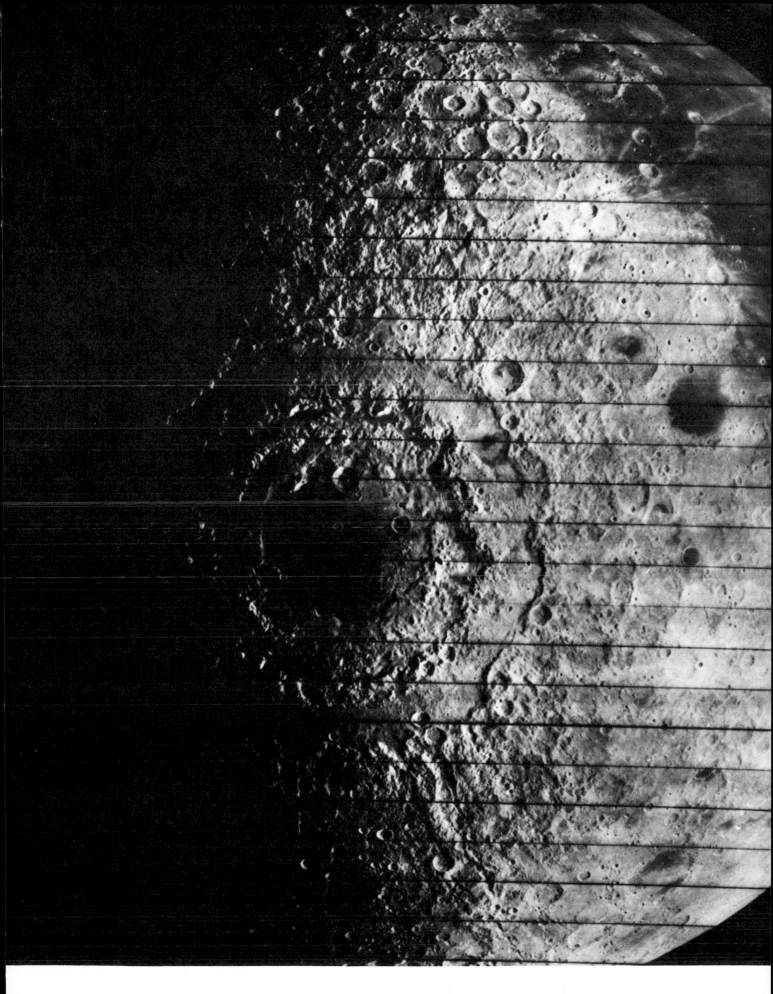

Details from
Robots on the Moon

When the first men to land on the moon looked around they found a surface of rocks and fine particles. This was no surprise because scientists had observed and analysed them by remote control. Robot space craft had landed gently on the moon, dug into its surface, tested the material chemically and magnetically, and televised

close-ups. The clear picture above is a mosaic of views taken by one of these craft, Surveyor V, when it landed in Mare Tranquillitatis (Sea of Tranquillity) on the 11th September, 1967, not far from the site where men first landed two years later. The camera swung completely round to reveal not only the dusty surface of the moon, but also to pick up parts of the space craft (*far left and far right*) and its shadow (*centre*); the moon's horizon appears against the blackness of space in an unnatural curve because the camera was tilted.

The findings of the American and Russian probes provided the first convincing evidence that the moon's surface, like the earth's, was made in part of basalt, a dark volcanic rock. One robot had a magnet that attracted soil particles near the surface, showing the presence of iron. Such robots may land in the future at spots where man will not be able to set foot and uncover an enormous wealth of information that could not otherwise be obtained.

Man's First Step on to Another World

On the 21st July, 1969, astronauts Neil Armstrong and Buzz Aldrin stood where no man had gone before and looked around at the surface of the moon. Although they spent only two and a half hours there and ventured no farther than about 200 feet from their landing capsule, they brought back information that provided scientists with many years of research.

Most intriguing of the approximately 100 pictures were those made with a special stereoscopic camera mounted on a walking stick. When taking a photograph, the astronauts pulled a trigger at the top—bending over in a space suit is impossible. These stereo pairs, in colour and finely detailed, revealed splashes of glassy material apparently vacuum plated with metals. Dust and rocks were brought back to earth in two sealed aluminium boxes. Analysis confirmed earlier evidence that they were igneous—created at high temperatures. But unlike earth rocks, they contained a very high proportion of titanium. What they did not contain was any sign of life or organic molecules. Germ-free mice exposed to moon samples were not affected.

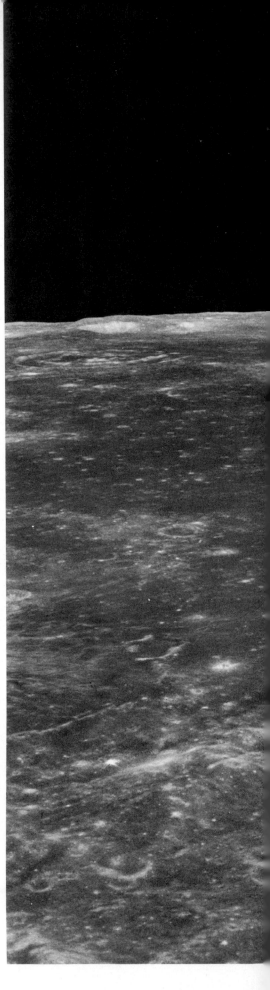

TRAPPING THE SOLAR WIND
Close by the bug-like Lunar Module of Apollo 11, Aldrin sets up a 40-inch strip of aluminium foil to trap atomic particles emitted by the sun in the "solar wind". The particles from space travel easily to the surface of the moon since they are not impeded by an atmosphere as they are on earth. The foil was brought back to earth to be analysed for particles that stuck to it.

MISSION ACCOMPLISHED
Having left their footprints on the moon, the astronauts ascend in the Lunar Module to rendezvous with the mother ship for the return to earth (*above the lunar horizon*). Stowed in their cabin are the priceless souvenirs of their visit: 48 pounds of lunar rocks, a particle-riddled strip of foil and about 100 photographs that promise new answers to the age-old puzzles of the moon.

5

The Mystery of the Clouded Body

A 4,000-year-old Babylonian tablet, found in the 19th century, records Venus's movements.

WHEN THE FIRST TELESCOPES were turned on the planet Venus in the early 17th century, there was good reason to hope for startling discoveries. Venus is the third brightest object in the sky, exceeded only by the sun and moon, and of all the planets it comes nearest to the earth. If it were really a world like the earth, as astronomers of the time had begun to believe, it ought to show many wonders, perhaps "seas" and "continents" like the moon's, perhaps even inhabitants.

Venus showed nothing of the sort. It is a sad disappointment to the visual observer. It passes through phases like the moon's because its orbit between the earth and sun makes different amounts of its illuminated hemisphere visible at different times, but the phases are about the only interesting thing that can be seen. Venus has no satellites like Jupiter, no rings like Saturn, no ice caps like Mars. All it shows to the eye at the telescope is a bright, slightly yellowish cloud deck that effectively hides its surface. Astronomers soon tired of staring at this featureless wrapping, and most of them abandoned Venus as not worth further effort.

The cloud deck is still a barrier to observation with optical telescopes, but Venus is no longer a hopeless enigma. Since 1956 an amazing amount has been learnt about its atmosphere and clouds, and even about the climate and topography of its hidden surface. Delicate new instruments were needed to extract faint clues from the cloud-shrouded planet, and subtle reasoning processes interpreted their meanings. The history of the campaign reads like a detective story, and its triumph is one of the great successes of modern astronomy.

Centuries of visual study had given Venus detectives precious little to build on. The orbit of Venus (about 67 million miles from the sun) was easy to calculate from repeated observations, but its mass was more elusive. The mass of a planet is calculated from its gravitational effect. The handiest method is to measure the distance and orbital period of a satellite, then insert these two figures in the proper equation derived from Newton's law of gravitation, which gives the mass of the parent body. But Venus has no satellite, so its mass had to be calculated from the effect of its gravitation on other bodies. The planet's size gave trouble too. Since nothing could be seen except the cloud deck—whose altitude was unknown—the diameter of the planet itself could not be measured with confidence.

From properties of the atmosphere the height of the clouds has been estimated, permitting the diameter to be determined with some accuracy. Venus turns out to be almost a twin of the earth so far as size is concerned. Its diameter is slightly less than the earth's at the equator (about 7,560 against 7,926 miles). Its mass is 81.4 per cent of the earth's, which makes its density less. Besides the unbroken clouds, Venus has an atmosphere so substantial that it is obvious even to visual observers. When Venus is passing directly between the earth and the sun, its illuminated face becomes a slender, diminishing crescent, and the tips of the crescent can be seen to extend until they become a faint ring of light enclosing the whole planet. This is the work of the atmosphere above the clouds, scattering sunlight around the planet.

Most other observations with ordinary telescopes proved of little help to the Venus detectives. Some observers saw faint shadings on the clouds; others saw none. Since there are no permanent markings to watch as they turn with the planet, the rotation of Venus could not be measured, and the positions of the poles and equator remained unknown.

The soda-water sea

The first big break in the case of the cloud-covered planet came in 1932, when spectroscopy found evidence of large amounts of carbon dioxide in its atmosphere. Improved hypotheses were constructed from this single clue, including the intriguing concept of a planet covered with a sea of soda water or, alternatively, petroleum. But no firm information was available about the hidden surface until the new techniques of radio astronomy found ways to measure the temperature under the clouds.

The temperature of the cloud deck itself had already been determined in two independent ways. Venus is nearer the sun than the earth is, and it receives about twice as much solar radiation, but its clouds are so bright that they reflect about 70 per cent of the sunlight back into space. Starting with this fact and assuming that the rest of the sunlight is absorbed by the clouds, astronomers are able to make a theoretical estimate of the temperature of the clouds, which comes out as $-40°C$. Direct measurements by infra-red light show that the clouds are actually very close to this theoretical temperature. If they contain water at this temperature, it must be in the form of ice crystals.

The two estimates of cloud-deck temperature confirmed each other nicely, but they did not cast any light on conditions below the clouds. Then, in 1956, radio astronomers detected three-centimetre (about one inch) microwaves coming from Venus. This wave length is absorbed by very few materials, so it is presumably able to pass through both the atmosphere and the clouds. The three-centimetre waves seem to originate in the hidden surface. Since the intensity of radiation can be used to tell the temperature of its source, calculations quickly showed that the surface of Venus, as revealed by the microwaves, must be at least as hot as $315°C$. Later observations showed even higher temperatures. In some places the surface must get hot enough to glow a deep, dull red.

Here was a startling picture: a red-hot planet wrapped in clouds of ice! The Venus detectives took a long breath and began to think of the planet as having a very deep atmosphere with very hot lower levels above a glowing surface. Then some scientists had an alternative idea. Perhaps, they speculated, the microwaves do not come from the surface; they may come from the ionosphere of Venus, many miles above the cloud deck. At this level, solar ultra-violet light and high-energy solar particles have detached electrons from gas atoms, creating charged particles called ions. Such a gas is called ionized, and it gives off microwaves when its electrically charged particles are attracted towards or repelled by each other. If the ionosphere of Venus could be shown to be about a thousand times richer in ions than the earth's, the microwave emission at three centimetres and longer might come from it, not from any hot surface far below.

The red-hot surface, then, might be an illusion. A further calculation of temperature could be made from microwaves very much shorter, a few tenths of an inch long, that also come from Venus. This calculation assumes that they arise from the lower atmosphere and can pass through the ionosphere. The temperature of the lower atmosphere deduced in this way is about 77° C., and the actual surface was thought to be close to the same temperature. It would be uncomfortably hot by the earth's climatic standards but not wholly impossible for the kind of life that has evolved on the earth. Some parts of Venus, especially the poles, might be considerably cooler and quite hospitable to earthly kinds of life.

Human wishful thinking was all on the side of this "cool" concept of the planet. Generations of dreamers had pictured Venus as having a reasonable climate and many fascinating plants and animals under its bright clouds, and few astronomers wanted to believe that the earth's nearest planetary neighbour might actually be hot enough on its surface to destroy all living things, as if they were bacon charred black in an unwatched frying-pan.

And then in 1962 the U.S. space craft Mariner II completed a spectacular 109-day voyage to Venus and observed the planet from a distance of 21,600 miles. On board were instruments sensitive to microwaves and infra-red light, and the data they gathered during the fly-past were sent by radio to the earth, 37 million miles away.

The hot and cool Venus

For the purpose of deciding between the hot and cool concepts of Venus, the key instrument was a detector tuned to pick up waves that could originate in the planet's ionosphere. The detector measured these waves as they were received from two directions—from a direct path to the bottom of the atmosphere, and from an oblique path through the other part of the atmosphere. The oblique path, being longer, included more of the ionosphere layer; thus, if Venus had a dense ionosphere, as the cool hypothesis demanded, the oblique path would furnish a greater amount of the waves than the direct path. Just the opposite was observed. Mariner II reported that as it scanned Venus it received more waves directly than obliquely. This result implies that Venus does not have an ionosphere sufficiently dense to be the source of its microwave emission. But such a microwave-emitting layer is a necessary part of the cool view of the planet and its absence means that Venus does not have a cool surface under the clouds. Most of the planet's surface is almost red-hot. A different set of instruments on Mariner V supported this conclusion in 1967, and in the same year the Soviet space craft Venera IV sent into the atmosphere of Venus a capsule that reported temperature by radio. Although it did not reach the surface of Venus, its findings indicated that the surface temperature could not be much lower than had been measured earlier by other methods. Veneras V and VI shared the fate of their predecessor and failed to survive the journey through the hot, pressurized Venusian atmosphere, but Venera VII, launched late in 1970, scored a signal success. After a 35-minute descent it made man's first material contact with the surface of Venus. For 23 minutes after landing, its instruments radioed signals reporting temperatures of 453° to 495°C. and pressures of about 90 atmospheres.

The next task of the Venus detectives was to explain why the surface is so hot. The only plausible source of the heat is sunlight, and the most likely mechanism for concentrating it is the "greenhouse effect", which operates to a lesser extent in the atmosphere of the earth.

The greenhouse effect takes its name from the familiar florist's greenhouse, a handy device to trap solar energy and thereby keep the temperature inside above that of the air outdoors. When sunlight passes through the glass roof, it mildly warms the plants and soil that it hits. They radiate some of this heat back, but since their temperature is relatively low, the radiation they emit towards the sky is long in wavelength. These long wave-lengths are blocked by the glass, but their heat energy cannot escape and the temperature rises inside the greenhouse.

A greenhouse in the sky

On Venus the role of the greenhouse glass could be played by the deep, dense atmosphere—if it contained enough heat-stopping materials. No single substance in it has enough blocking effect to make the surface red-hot. Some of the infra-red wave-lengths that try to escape into space are blocked by the carbon dioxide that is known to exist in the atmosphere of Venus, but other wave-lengths not stopped by carbon dioxide would carry heat away, unless they were stopped by something else.

Water vapour could do that—if it were really present on Venus. All early attempts to detect it, however, were utter failures. The main trouble was the water vapour in the earth's atmosphere, which tended to hide any clues to water that might be offered by spectra of the feeble sunlight reflected from Venus. The difficulty was finally sidestepped by attaching an infra-red spectrometer to a balloon to carry it above most of the earth's water vapour. The experiment showed that the atmosphere of Venus does contain water vapour and the Soviet capsule reported just the right amount to trap additional heat and account for the planet's high surface temperature. The goodly amount of water in the atmosphere indicates that the tops of the clouds must be made of ice particles, not of dust or other solid matter.

At the subsolar point (the place where sunlight falls vertically), the temperature may rise to 700°C. Elsewhere, however, temperatures could be different, influenced by factors in addition to solar heat. Are there cooler polar regions? Do conditions change during the seasons, or from day to night? Before such questions could be answered by theory, the Venus detectives had to find out how fast Venus rotates.

The most obvious way to determine rotation is to watch the surface markings moving across the face of a planet, but this did not work for Venus, whose clouds hide all the surface markings and have no lasting markings of their own. Equally fruitless were attempts to use spectroscopes and conventional telescopes to measure rotation by the so-called Doppler shift—which refers to the fact that waves of light reflected from an approaching body are shortened, while those reflected from a retreating body are lengthened. In each case the size of the shift in wave-length tells how fast the body is approaching or moving away. If light is reflected from the edge of a rotating sphere, its Doppler shift tells how fast the surface is moving towards or away from the observer, and therefore tells the sphere's speed of rotation.

Spectroscopic study of the Doppler shift works well with many stars and most planets, but although it was often tried on Venus, using the world's best optical telescopes, it never succeeded. Sunlight reflected from the edges of the planet's disc stubbornly refused to show any shift. All these negative results indicated that Venus rotated very slowly, if at all. Until recently the most common opinion was that it always kept the same face towards the sun, just as the moon keeps the same face towards the earth.

The first positive information about the rotation of Venus came in the early 1960's from the rapidly improving techniques of radar astronomy. When a beam of microwaves is turned on Venus, most of the echo that returns is reflected from a small area in the centre of the planet where the surface is almost perpendicular to the incoming waves. Weaker echoes come from the edges of the planet, and their wave-lengths, which can be measured very precisely, show small but distinct Doppler shifts —strong evidence that the edges of the planet move; Venus rotates.

The wrong-way planet

The story the microwaves told about Venus was exciting to all astronomers. With the exception of Uranus, all planets whose rotation is known have what is called "direct" rotation. This means that they rotate in the same direction in which they revolve in their orbits around the sun. Venus, however, is different. Radar astronomy proves that its rotation is "retrograde"; like a wheel spinning backwards, it turns in the wrong direction. No one knows the reason for this planetary perversity, but astronomers welcome it as a new and fascinating mystery. Its solution might well cast some light on the way in which the solar system was formed.

Venus's retrograde rotation is very slow. It turns on its axis about once in 243 earth days. Since its orbit around the sun takes 224.7 days, the combination of the two motions makes sunrise take place on Venus at intervals of about 118 earth days.

Determination of the planet's rotation period was an important break for the Venus detectives. It indicated to them that Venus should have notable changes of temperature during its long day. So it turned out. Careful analysis of radio waves, which are believed to come from just below the surface, shows that the surface on the dark night side may cool down by as much as 400°C. When the subsolar point is at 700°C., the temperature of the anti-solar point—in the centre of the dark hemisphere —is about 320°C. The polar regions may be even cooler, perhaps as cool as 200°C. This temperature is above the boiling point of water on the earth (100°C. at sea level). But since the atmospheric pressure on Venus is much greater, raising the boiling point, there is a bare possibility that water can exist as a liquid near the comparatively cool poles. It would not be much like the water in the earth's oceans. It would be more like the violent stuff confined in a power-plant boiler in full operation.

Without a co-ordinated series of "soft" landings on Venus, trying to determine what the surface is like under the unbroken clouds might seem hopeless. And yet the subtle techniques of the new radio astronomy have gathered a surprising amount of information by analysing the lengths of waves emitted by the surface. The longer waves are believed to come from greater depths than the short ones, and they reveal that the deeper material has a more stable temperature, not heating as much by day or cooling as much at night. At a depth of about a yard, the temperature variation is already very small. This means that the surface material must be a very good heat insulator, better than nearly all solid rocks. Therefore, large areas of Venus must be covered with finely pulverized dust, which has about the right insulating properties.

Mountains on Venus

Radar-astronomy has made the extraordinary discovery that mountain ranges and large craters, or something that looks very much like them, exist on the surface of Venus. These objects do not show themselves directly, like ships or aeroplanes, on the scope of a military radar. Venus is so far away that any existing beam of radar waves spreads out so much that it cannot concentrate on a portion of the planet. The echo that comes back has been reflected from an entire hemisphere, and it must be analysed in complicated ways before it yields information about details on the hidden surface of the planet.

The first step in this involved series of deductions requires the location of the general areas reflecting parts of the beam—a seemingly impossible task that is accomplished by extremely delicate clocking of the echoes. The waves reflected by the nearest part of Venus, the centre of the hemisphere facing earth, will get back to the earth first, followed by waves from more distant parts. The edges of the disc, which are about 4,000 miles farther from the earth than the centre is, will be heard from last. These time delays can be measured very accurately to identify the area that is being heard from. In this way the echoes are traced to successively larger and more distant ring-shaped zones on the planet.

Such rough locations of the sources of the echoes can then be com-

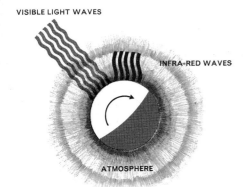

VISIBLE LIGHT WAVES

INFRA-RED WAVES

ATMOSPHERE

THE GREENHOUSE EFFECT which warms the earth may similarly exist on Venus. The effect begins when short, visible light waves from the sun penetrate the atmosphere during the day. As the planet's surface absorbs them, it heats up and radiates long, infra-red waves which are then trapped by the atmosphere and clouds, just as they would be by the glass walls of a greenhouse. If none of the infra-red waves escaped, the surface temperature would increase indefinitely. But on earth enough of them do escape to maintain a balance with the incoming sunlight, stabilizing the temperature of the earth's surface at about 30°C. higher than it would be without the greenhouse effect.

bined with measurements of the intensities of the echoes to reveal surface prominences. If Venus were perfectly uniform all over its surface, the amounts of energy reflected by each of the concentric zones would follow a pattern predicted by theory. This is not what happens. Some of the zones return more energy than they theoretically should, indicating that they contain one or more highly reflective regions. By analysing the time delay in the radar signal, scientists can place these highly reflective regions within particular zones. The true position within each zone can then be estimated because the reflecting area moves as the planet rotates, and the reflected waves therefore exhibit a Doppler shift, which can be measured. This complex technique permits a crude map of Venus to be drawn. Radar astronomers have become so clever at this sort of thing that they can watch certain reflective objects appearing at one edge of the cloud-covered planet, moving slowly towards the centre and disappearing over the opposite edge.

It is these reflective objects that some observers have identified as mountain ranges resembling those on the earth. One range, called the Alpha mountains, is perhaps 2,400 miles long and runs roughly north and south, while the Beta mountains run east-west and may be even longer. Both Alpha and Beta seem to be several hundred miles across and show hints of a complex structure. They may be made of multiple ridges, as the earth's mountains often are. Or they may have a kind of topography unknown to the earth and not yet identified elsewhere in the solar system.

Ice crystals above a red-hot surface

The Venus detectives have now collected enough information about the planet to give some idea of its climate and scenery. The atmosphere is heavy, 30 times or so as dense as the earth's, so even gentle winds will raise dust storms. Roughly 40 miles above the surface hang the eternal clouds made of ice crystals on their tops and water droplets lower down. If there are breaks in the clouds, the clear sky that shows through has a yellowish-green tinge. The sun, in its rare "appearances", is deep brick red. Violent storms may toss the clouds into towering billows, but any rain that falls from them evaporates in the hot, dry atmosphere before it comes near the ground.

Most of the planet's surface is rather smooth, probably made of loose dust glowing dull red in shadows and hot enough to char any organic matter. Exposed rocky surfaces may be wind-eroded, showing curved and hollowed shapes like rocks exposed to sand-laden winds on the earth's waterless deserts, but this is by no means certain.

Besides its atmosphere and surface, so different from the earth's, Venus seems to have a different interior. Instruments carried by Mariner II showed that its magnetic field is weak or non-existent, and this is fairly good evidence that it does not have a core of liquid iron like the earth's. It is likely that iron was plentiful in the original material of which the planet was formed; if the iron did not migrate towards the centre, as most

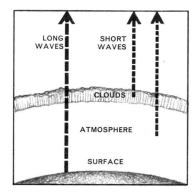

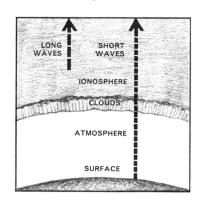

TWO MODELS OF VENUS have been postulated to explain the fact that the planet emits both long and short radio waves. Some observers once favoured an "ionospheric model" (*below*), showing a relatively cool (93° C.) surface which radiates short waves and a thick ionosphere which radiates long waves. But data transmitted by Mariner II during its 1962 flight past Venus have convinced astronomers that the ionosphere is not dense enough to produce long waves. They now favour a "greenhouse model" (*top*), where the planet's surface, heated to more than 426° C. by the greenhouse effect (*opposite*), radiates the long waves, while the short waves come from the atmosphere and clouds.

of the earth's iron did, it may have stayed close enough to the surface to combine with oxygen, thus accounting for the absence of oxygen in the atmosphere.

Venus is now known to be so hot and dry that there is little hope of finding life on its surface. Even if a little liquid water exists near the poles, it will be hot enough to destroy the complex organic compounds, such as proteins and nucleic acids, which are the chemical basis of the earth's life. There may be different kinds of life elsewhere in the universe, but the heat of Venus would probably be fatal to them too.

There is a small possibility, of course, that Venus was cooler in the remote past and had liquid water in which life developed. If living organisms did appear, they might have evolved fast enough to adapt themselves to the increasingly hostile climate, perhaps by taking refuge in the clouds, and thus to stay alive.

But such possibilities seem unlikely. When a heat-proofed space probe is sent from the earth to the searing surface of Venus, it will probably find no life and no sign that life ever existed there. Organic molecules from the early history of the solar system will be absent also. The heat of Venus will not preserve them as the deep freeze of the moon would.

Colonizing Venus

And yet, dead as it seems today, Venus need not be written off for ever as an abode for life. It is potentially fertile. It has water, carbon dioxide and light, the essential requirements for photosynthesis. Nitrogen, essential to earthly life, probably forms the bulk of its atmosphere. All the minor elements needed by life, such as phosphorus, magnesium, etc., are believed to exist in its dusty surface. So although Venus may be unable to develop life of its own, it offers a possible field for colonization from the earth. This might be attempted after an intermediate period of what can be called "microbiological planetary engineering".

No one who has studied the swarming, varied life of the earth fails to be impressed with its amazing ability to adapt itself to a wide range of environments. Micro-organisms thrive in hot springs, on snowfields, in saturated brines, in the pressure, dark and cold of ocean beds. It is not inconceivable that an organism can be found or developed that will live and thrive somewhere on Venus and, in time, make it inhabitable for higher forms of life.

The one place in Venus where colonies of living things might be planted is in the clouds. Their bottom levels probably contain water droplets at a temperature of about $-9°$ C., providing conditions which, laboratory experiments indicate, may support life. To be suited to life in the clouds of Venus, the microcolonists must be able to extract water from the clouds or the atmosphere and turn gaseous nitrogen into nitrogen compounds for use in their body chemistry. They must live a wholly aerial life, suspended by the turbulence that stirs the clouds. They must resist ultra-violet light and reproduce rapidly whenever carried to places where conditions are favourable.

These seem tough requirements, but the earth's micro-organisms have recently shown what they can do by adapting themselves in a few years to remarkably hostile new conditions. Some of them have set up house-keeping in the fuel tanks of jet planes, where they live on kerosene and do not seem to be bothered by violent changes of pressure and temperature. Another group has learned to live in the cooling water that circulates through the cores of nuclear reactors, where the radiation would kill a human being quickly.

Such achievements by the earth's humblest inhabitants are encouraging to the microbiological planetary engineers, who hope that scientifically selected organisms will do even better. The most promising species to start with are blue-green algae, which already have many of the needed abilities. If they are subjected in the laboratory to increasingly rigorous conditions for years or decades, strains may emerge that can thrive in the clouds of Venus. Transporting them to their new home will not be difficult, even with existing space vehicles.

According to one speculation, the arrival of micro-organisms on Venus may have a dramatic effect on the planet. Once they are established and begin to multiply rapidly, they will abstract large quantities of water and carbon dioxide from their cloud homes and will break down these substances by photosynthesis, manufacturing food and discharging oxygen into the atmosphere. The bulk of the organic matter that they make in this way will be carbohydrates, which can be considered as combinations of carbon and water. When any of the micro-organisms fall into the hot lower atmosphere or are carried there by down-currents, they will be charred to black carbon by the heat. The water in them will be released to return to the atmosphere while the carbon will be deposited on the surface far below.

Making Venus habitable

If these reactions continue long enough—and this need not be very long—they will take much of the carbon dioxide out of the atmosphere, replacing it with oxygen. Since the high temperature of the surface depends in part on the greenhouse effect of carbon dioxide, the surface will then cool down. If it gets cool enough for rain to collect at the poles as liquid water, the greenhouse effect of water vapour in the atmosphere will be reduced also, causing additional cooling. When more rain falls, the heat-retaining clouds will partially clear away, leaving a planet with an oxygen-rich atmosphere and a temperature cool enough to sustain hardy plants and animals from the earth. It may even be suitable for human colonization.

Human colonies for an ice-clouded, red-hot planet may seem fantastic. But the fact that such a prospect can now be entertained is a tribute to the power of the astronomer's techniques, which have revealed the topography, climate and atmosphere of a planet whose surface no man has seen. From 36 million miles away, ingenious instruments and sophisticated deduction are solving the mystery of the veiled planet.

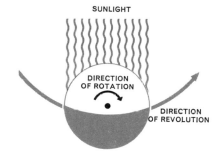

THE ROTATION OF VENUS around its axis presents astronomers with a mystery they cannot yet explain. When viewed from above their north poles, most planets (e.g., earth) rotate counter-clockwise, or directly (*below*) —the same way as they revolve round the sun. But Venus's rotation (*above*) is clockwise, or retrograde, and opposite to the way it revolves round the sun.

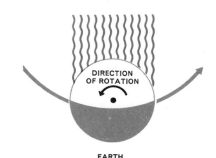

Venus:
Roasting under Ice

An old fable tells of a blind man who felt an elephant's tail and concluded the animal was made of rope, while another grabbed its trunk and described it as a snake and another felt a leg and decided it was like a tree. Astronomers have had the same trouble with Venus. No one has ever seen its cloud-shrouded surface, and for centuries there were not enough facts to draw a picture from. Galileo discovered the planet's phases (*right*) in 1610, but that gave no hint about its physical appearance. The presence of an atmosphere was deduced in 1761. Until recently, little else was known.

Speculation based on such scanty information produced an intriguing variety of concepts. One writer thought Venus was populated by reptiles. Others saw it as a steamy swamp, as a place enveloped by dust clouds, as a sea of carbonated water, or as an ocean of oil. Only by arming themselves with instruments that can "see" through the clouds have astronomers finally been able to start solving the puzzle of Venus. With data from radar, radio telescopes, infra-red detectors and space vehicles they are now able to draw with some confidence a picture of Earth's mysterious neighbour.

EXPLAINING THE PHASES
An explanation of the phases of Venus and Mercury was drawn in 1643 by the Swiss mathematician Matthias Hirzgarter. As the planets travel round the sun, half the surface of each is always illuminated; but since their orbits are inside the earth's, the visible portion of their lighted surfaces, as seen by an observer on the earth, gradually decreases as they approach the earth.

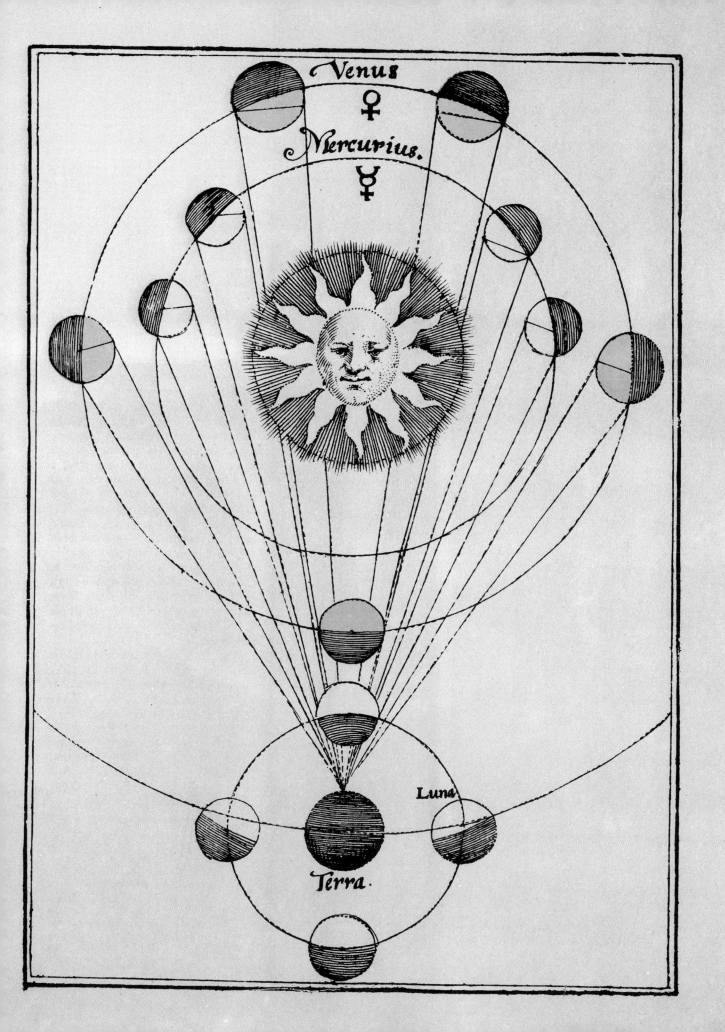

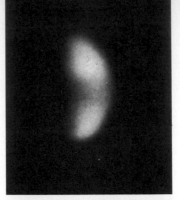

Charting the Unknown

The optical telescopes which have revealed so many secrets in the skies are very little help in solving the puzzle of Venus. They revealed its dense atmosphere and help to plot the planet's phases as it swings between the earth and the sun every 584 days; and some astronomers have thought they have seen through a telescope shadowy markings on the planet's cloud layer. But observers seldom agree on what they have seen, and no visible-light photographs have ever confirmed their findings.

But that there are shadings of some sort within the cloud layer has been proved by ultra-violet photographs, pictures taken on film sensitive to radiations whose wave-length is just a little shorter than visible light. These markings indicate billows or multiple cloud layers in the upper atmosphere of Venus.

A start has also been made in the much more difficult job of charting the planet's surface. The key tool is radar, which bounces signals off Venus and analyses the faint echoes. Radar not only has enabled astronomers to probe the planet's hidden topography but has told them that Venus rotates the "wrong" way, that its day is about 250 earth days long and it has, in effect, only one season.

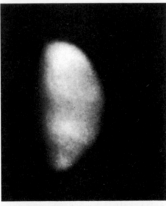

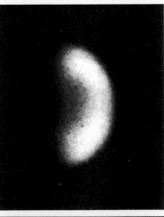

PHASES FROM FULL TO CRESCENT

Venus, seen through a telescope, appears full when it is on the far side of the sun. As it nears earth it becomes a thin crescent. Then, almost between the earth and the sun (*bottom*), Venus is distinguished by a fuzzy partial halo created as sunlight is scattered by its atmosphere.

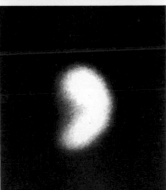

VENUS BY ULTRA-VIOLET

Ultra-violet photographs, taken at Lowell Observatory in Arizona, reveal dark patches in the clouds of Venus. The patches change in appearance and position from day to day, suggesting that they may be caused by billowings in the planet's cloud layer, produced by strong winds.

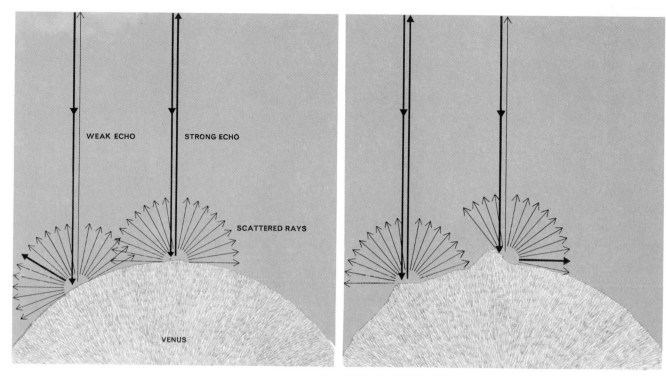

WEAK ECHO STRONG ECHO

SCATTERED RAYS

VENUS

MAPPING BY RADAR

The tentative map of Venus below is based on interpretations of radar signals as illustrated above. On the left above, the signals are shown bouncing off a smooth surface. Only the centre of the curved surface reflects a strong echo (*thick arrow*) back to earth. Where the surface curves away the rays bounce off at an angle, so that the planet's edges return only weak signals to earth. If, however, the radar rays bounce off irregularities such as mountains, the patterns are changed (*right, above*). In what is otherwise an area of weak echoes, strong ones come bouncing back from the oblique surface; radar rays striking at a different angle bounce their strongest signals off to one side, and only weak scattered signals return to earth. In the map below, the dark area indicates the range of normal strong echoes, gradually weakening away from the central area. To the west (*right*) something has sent back stronger echoes than anticipated. This area is called the Beta mountains. Whether it actually is a mountain range or some other topographical feature will have to await the results from future Venus probes.

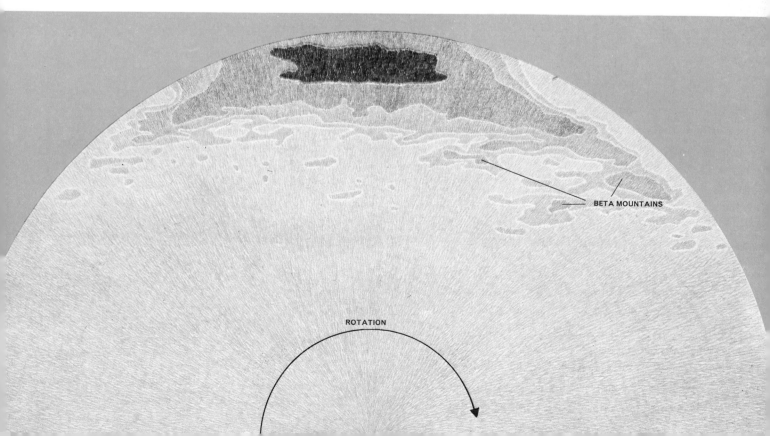

BETA MOUNTAINS

ROTATION

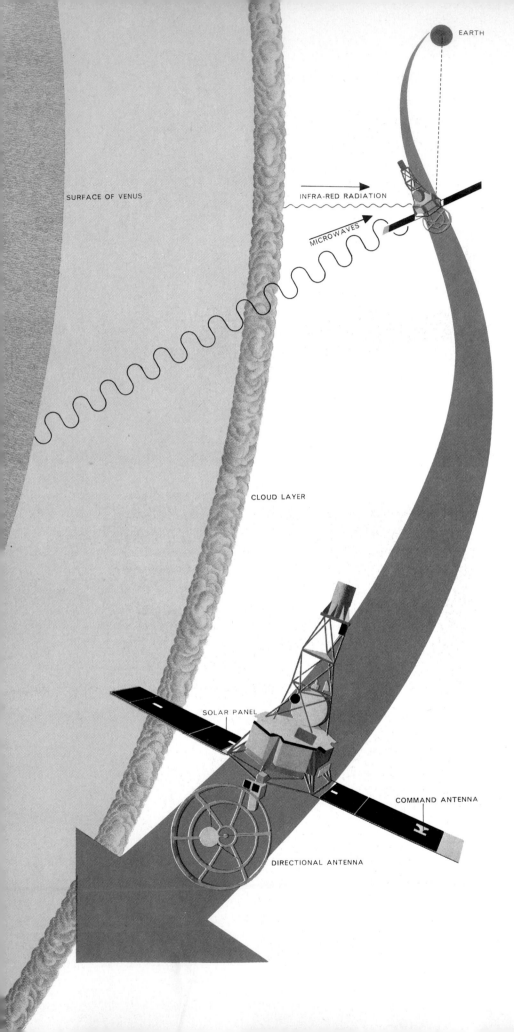

SURFACE OF VENUS

EARTH

INFRA-RED RADIATION

MICROWAVES

CLOUD LAYER

SOLAR PANEL

COMMAND ANTENNA

DIRECTIONAL ANTENNA

First Report from Out There

In December of 1962 the unmanned spacecraft Mariner II performed what was at the time man's most impressive space feat: the first close-up look at another planet. From 21,600 miles away, Mariner radioed back a report on Venus that, while far from comprehensive, carried information that no earth-mounted telescope, radar or camera had provided.

Two important parts of Mariner's report came from compact detectors designed to pick up certain microwaves, which gave information about surface temperatures, and infra-red radiation, which provided data on the temperature of the cloud cover. Astronomers hoped that Mariner II could detect variations in intensity of the radiation that would determine whether Venus's high-temperature readings came from its atmosphere or its surface. They were not disappointed. Mariner, operating on command, obediently took its readings from several different angles and settled a long-standing argument: Venus's surface is extremely hot (averaging about 430° C.), but its cloud layer is very cold (averaging −40°C.).

A FAST FLY-BY

After a 109-day trip covering 180 million miles, Mariner II spent 35 minutes "listening in" on Venus before continuing in its long orbit round the sun. Its detectors monitored radiation which confirmed the planet's surface and cloud-layer temperatures; Mariner II also discovered that Venus has no apparent magnetic field, and that, unlike earth, it has no enveloping belt of charged particles. These findings were beamed to earth by Mariner II's directional antenna (shown reversed for this illustration); orders from the earth were received by the command antenna.

A DUSTLESS CHECK-UP

Surgically garbed technicians in a dust-free chamber prepare Mariner II for its trip to Venus. The 447-pound craft, partially coated with gold and aluminium as protection against the sun's heat, has 10,700 solar cells which convert sunlight into electrical power for the equipment.

Two Versions of Venus

Before modern astronomical instruments began to unlock Venus's secrets, scientists relied mostly on educated guesswork to concoct descriptions of the planet's surface.

In 1918, a Swedish chemist named Svante August Arrhenius suggested that the clouds veiling the planet must be composed of water, as are Earth's clouds, and that the planet must be a vast swamp (*below, left*), resembling the swamps of the earth's Carboniferous era some 280 million years ago. Arrhenius concluded that temperatures, averaging about 50° C., caused vegetation to grow at such a furious rate that plants died rapidly and their decaying bodies filled the air with stifling gases. Beneath the swamps he envisaged great beds of coal. Arrhenius was vague about the possibilities of animal life. He did say, however, that "progress and culture" were more likely at the poles than at the hotter equator.

In 1922 the American astronomers

A STEAMY SWAMP

Charles St. John and Seth B. Nicholson revolted against the "wet Venus" theory, and formulated an hypothesis that stands up better today than even some more recent ones. After painstaking spectroscopic study of light absorption by molecules in the planet's atmosphere, they concluded there was "no appreciable amount" of water vapour or oxygen on Venus (recent studies have suggested that traces of water exist both above and below the clouds). They sug-gested that the surface of Venus was a wind-swept desert (*below, right*), and the clouds were great billows of dust swept up by furious winds circling the planet. Their concept was quite different from Arrhenius's, because they had one more piece of data to work with. And their final speculation—that the atmosphere of Venus may contain considerable carbon dioxide—was proved correct a decade later when large amounts of carbon dioxide were indeed discovered.

A DUSTY DESERT

A Seltzer Sea,
an Oily Ocean

When a spectroscopic study in 1932 detected abundant carbon dioxide in the atmosphere of Venus, astronomers acquired a key fact on which to base their speculations about the planet. By 1955, two new models of Venus had been devised to take into account the discovery.

The first tried to explain the carbon dioxide in terms of one theory about the earth's atmosphere. On earth great quantities of carbon dioxide have been released from the in-terior, but most of the gas has combined with silicate materials to form carbonates like limestone or chalk. Why hadn't this happened on Venus? Some astronomers hypothesized that the surface of Venus might be almost entirely covered with water (*below, left*), leaving nothing to use up the carbon dioxide. The water would be charged with carbon dioxide, forming a seltzer-water sea. Islands thrusting above the surface would have lime-stone crusts, and erosion would grad-

A CARBONATED SEA

ually wear them down to the surface.

The other hypothesis offered a different explanation of how the carbon dioxide got into Venus's atmosphere. It argued that Venus at one time had some water and vast amounts of oily hydrocarbons, perhaps like petroleum. Ultra-violet rays from the sun split the water molecules into hydrogen and oxygen, and then the oily hydrocarbons combined with the oxygen to form carbon dioxide. Eventually, all the water was used up, and nothing was left but carbon dioxide and huge quantities of hydrocarbons forming a vast ocean of oil, possibly bubbling with natural gas. "Venus is probably endowed beyond the dreams of the richest Texas oil-king", said one proponent of the concept. In this model of Venus the clouds consist of a heavy smog of oily droplets, instead of water droplets. Since practically nothing was known then about the make-up of Venus's clouds, the hypothesis was not unreasonable.

A PETROLEUM PLANET

A Forbidding Picture

After 1956 a more reliable picture of Venus began to emerge—a surprising picture of a searingly hot, bone-dry planet surrounded by clouds made, perhaps, of ice. Radio-telescopes reported—and space probes confirmed—conditions so extreme as to rule out a surface of either water or oil: temperatures on the sunlit side averaging 426°C., with a high of 700°C.

The heavy layer of carbon dioxide and water vapour in the atmosphere of Venus acts as an enormously effective blanket, holding in the heat of the sun. The atmospheric pressure under this cloak is about 100 times that of the earth's surface—the equivalent of the pressure exerted on a submarine some 3,000 feet down. No erosive water can exist, but thousands of millions of years of wind-borne sand erosion have probably sculpted any existing rocks into eerie shapes resembling the strange formations called yardangs found in some deserts of Central Asia.

If the planet's covering of clouds is mostly ice and dust, some sunlight may filter through. In shadowed areas the surface must glow red. So it seems that Venus is a very forbidding place. Except perhaps near the bottom of the clouds—a region that may be earth-like save for the absence of oxygen—Venus appears quite inhospitable to familiar forms of life.

6
The
Red
Planet

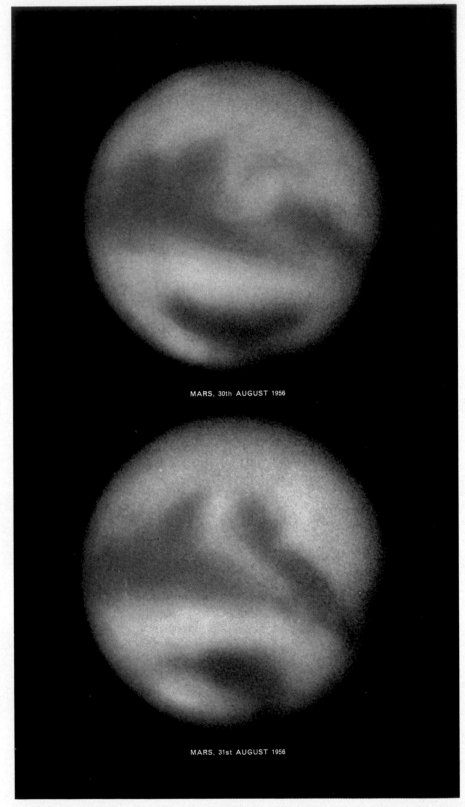

MARS, 30th AUGUST 1956

MARS, 31st AUGUST 1956

A huge dust storm (*top*) obscures Mars's normal face (*bottom*) in pictures taken a day apart.

FROM THE POINT OF VIEW of the earth's inquisitive inhabitants, the most interesting planet in many ways is Mars. Its atmosphere is thick enough to give it a climate and weather of a sort, but its clouds do not hide the surface the way the clouds of Venus do. Like the earth, it has white polar caps, and its surface changes shade with the advance of the seasons.

These earth-like properties have suggested strongly to some that Mars is inhabited by a kind of life not very different from that on Earth. Indeed, the planet has appeared, superficially, to be so hospitable that many writers, not all of them consciously writers of fiction, have peopled it with intelligent beings at least as advanced as man. While such an extreme view is not now favoured by the great majority of astronomers, many of them believe that Mars could maintain life. Recent observations have lessened but not eliminated this possibility. With respect to conditions favouring life, Mars is in a special class of its own.

The likelihood that life might exist on Mars does not depend on the planet's similarity to the earth. In major physical respects, Mars is less like the earth than Venus is. Its diameter (4,220 miles) is a little more than half of the earth's, and its mass is about one-tenth. It follows an orbit considerably more elliptical than the earth's, with a mean distance from the sun of about 140 million miles, more than 50 per cent greater than the earth's. Sunlight on Mars is, on the average, less than half as strong as on the earth, and this makes the planet much colder.

The features that suggest life on Mars are hard to see. In spite of its generally clear atmosphere, the planet is an exasperating target. Even through a large telescope it looks like a small, reddish-orange ball, fuzzy at the edges and usually shimmering slightly because of turbulence in the earth's atmosphere. The untrained eye sees little except the white polar caps, at least one of which is usually on view, and a few dark mottlings. But if the observer persists and is favoured by nights of good seeing, the fuzzy ball develops a personality. The dark blotches become familiar. They acquire sharper outlines and smaller markings appear between them. At last comes a rare instant when the air overhead stands still. The fuzzy ball snaps into sharp focus, revealing hundreds of small and varied details, far too many to be remembered. Then everything abruptly disappears, leaving the observer with the feeling of having just missed a glorious revelation. Frantically he sketches a few details, then eagerly looks forward to the next rare instant of perfect seeing.

Even the best photography does not catch these elusive glimpses because there is no way to anticipate the brief intervals of perfect seeing and take a picture at the right time. So until 1965, when the U.S. space craft Mariner IV took the first spectacular close-up pictures of Mars, the best detailed knowledge of the Martian surface was the product of years of patient work at the telescope by many highly skilled visual observers. Though their sketches were much more detailed than existing photographs, they were not always accurate or in agreement.

Out of this disagreement grew the great canal controversy, perhaps the gaudiest episode in the history of modern astronomy. In 1877 the Italian astronomer Giovanni Schiaparelli announced that he had observed on Mars a network of thin straight lines. He called them *canali*, which means "channels" in Italian. He did not claim they were artificial, and he may have been startled when the American astronomer Percival Lowell declared them to be "canals". They were, said Lowell firmly, irrigation canals dug by highly civilized Martians to transport water from the melting polar ice caps. The Martians, he explained in a series of articles, books and lectures, were in a difficult position. Their planet was drying up, and they had to make the best use of the remaining water.

The more Lowell studied Mars the more canals he saw; his later maps of the planet were cobwebbed with them. They were more than canals, he said. Actual watercourses were too narrow to be seen, but on both sides were cultivated fields where the Martians grew their irrigated crops. In certain places where the strips crossed were broad oases, presumably the major centres of Martian civilization.

The "cities" of Mars

This beguiling concept won passionate adherents who equipped Mars with everything that a civilized planet should have: ships on the canals, gorgeous cities in the oases and enormous engineering works to make the water flow. Lowell also had opponents who looked at Mars and saw nothing but vague light and dark patches uncrossed by any kind of line, straight or otherwise. Some of the most experienced visual observers took a middle position. Under superb seeing conditions they occasionally saw great numbers of mottled details on Mars but did not know what to make of them. They suspected that Lowell and his followers were glimpsing the same details at the far limit of vision and permitting their eyes or imaginations to string them together into straight "canals".

The canal enthusiasm died down when better instruments and subtler means of interpretation showed that conditions on Mars are far from compatible with a high civilization of earthly type. But the pictures transmitted to earth by space craft in the 1960s and 1970s showed that Mars is richer in detail than even Percival Lowell expected.

Just what is there on Mars? Even the crude view of Mars available from the earth shows diverse and changing conditions. Mars has several kinds of clouds in its atmosphere; it undergoes an annual march of the seasons, which seems to change the properties of large areas, and its topography may be as varied as the earth's.

As seen from the earth, the planet has three general types of surface. Most conspicuous are the dazzling white polar caps. The southern cap disappears entirely during the southern summer, but the northern cap always leaves a small patch when it, in turn, recedes.

Next in prominence are irregular areas of orange ochre that cover perhaps two-thirds of the planet. They are usually called deserts, though early observers often gave them idyllic names such as Elysium and Eden. Among them are darker patches that bear the names of bodies of water,

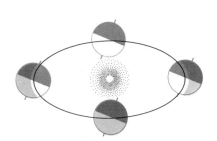

THE CHANGE OF SEASONS on a planet is due to the tilt of its axis of rotation. If the axis were perpendicular to the plane of its orbit, there would be no seasons. But when the axis is tilted, alternate hemispheres receive more than their share of solar radiation at different times of the year. For half a year, the north pole leans towards the sun, causing the sun's rays to strike the northern hemisphere (*blue area*) more directly. Then, for the rest of the year, the south pole leans towards the sun, and the southern hemisphere receives stronger sunlight.

like the moon's maria. They have sometimes been described as green, but detailed measurements show them to be primarily reddish like the adjacent bright areas—only darker. These are the parts of Mars that show the most interesting seasonal changes and have received the most rapt attention from astronomers.

Since the Martian axis is tipped at about the same angle as the earth's, Mars' polar regions are exposed to sunlight in alternation, just as the earth's are, giving each hemisphere summer and winter. But Mars takes 687 days to orbit the sun, which means that its year is a little less than two of our years long, and its seasons are double the length of the earth's.

Spring in reverse

The seasons bring remarkable surface changes on Mars, changes that are suggestive of those on earth. When spring comes to the earth's Northern Hemisphere, the snow cover in North America and northern Europe and Asia gradually shrinks, retreating towards the Pole, and a little later the land changes colour from south to north as grasses grow and deciduous trees put out new leaves. On Mars a rather similar change occurs but the direction is reversed. When one of its polar caps shrinks, a "wave of darkening" moves away from its retreating edge and advances towards the Martian equator at about 20 miles a day. This wave progressively darkens the dark areas as compared with near-by bright areas. It is tempting to conclude that water released by the shrinking cap has stimulated Martian vegetation into vigorous springtime growth. An observer with an active imagination can almost hear the Martian birds sing.

Attacks have been made on this attractive idea of burgeoning vegetation. Water is very scarce on Mars. The polar caps may be made, in part at least, of some form of frozen water deposited directly from water vapour like the frost on window-panes on cold winter nights. But Martian frost does not melt to form liquid water; the pressure of the atmosphere is so low that ice turns directly to water vapour without passing through the liquid stage, just as dry ice turns directly into carbon dioxide gas on earth. The springtime growth of Martian vegetation, if it takes place, must depend on the seasonal arrival of water vapour, not on anything like rain or freshets of liquid water.

The atmosphere has other properties that are not favourable to familiar kinds of life. It has long been known to be thin, but the three Mariner space craft proved it to be even thinner than had been supposed. As each began to pass behind Mars, its radio signals to earth briefly traversed deeper and deeper layers of the Martian atmosphere. Measurements of the fading of the radio waves enabled scientists to determine the atmospheric pressure at the surface. It is less than one per cent of the earth's and is apparently composed of carbon dioxide and a small amount of water vapour that is believed to vary in concentration from place to place but is never as abundant as over the earth's driest deserts. No oxygen or ozone has been detected in the Martian atmosphere. As a result, germicidal solar ultra-violet light—absorbed by oxygen and ozone on

A ROCK-LIKE MARS is shown in this 17th-century engraving by Matthias Hirzgarter. Hirzgarter, a Swiss mathematician, used data obtained from the Italian astronomer Francesco Fontana to postulate that the planet was a huge, triangular-shaped rock. Because of a faulty telescope, Fontana had mistaken certain dark markings on Mars—the Syrtis Major region—for the planet itself. The traditional symbol for Mars appears on the rock.

the earth—probably reaches the Martian surface at nearly full strength.

Though the Martian atmosphere supports clouds, some of ice crystals, others of yellowish dust, it does not contain enough heat-trapping gases to hold much of the sun's heat. It is not nearly as effective a "greenhouse" as the earth's atmosphere is. This, with the dryness of the surface, enables the scanty heat that reaches Mars from the sun to escape easily. The temperatures of the different zones can be measured separately by infra-red light and nowhere is the climate tolerable by human standards. Near the equator at noon the surface temperature may rise to 20° or nearly 30° C., but during the night it plunges to −85° C. The poles in winter are even colder. Radio-astronomy tells a similar story, indicating that about one foot below the surface the average temperature is an almost steady −60° C. The fact that the surface warmth does not penetrate more than a few inches suggests that Mars has a layer of insulating dust perhaps a little like the moon's.

Cratered surface

These conditions—cold, extreme dryness, intense ultra-violet light and lack of oxygen—are hostile to familiar forms of advanced life and the outlook was not improved by the first close view of the Martian surface, obtained by Mariner IV. When the space craft passed within 6,200 miles of Mars, its pictures showed circular shapes that are undoubtedly meteorite impact craters like those of the moon. These craters are of all sizes, from 3 to 75 miles in diameter, and apparently of different ages. The largest has only half its rim; the rest has been obliterated, though probably not by later impacts. Many of the craters are shallow, round depressions without visible raised rims and are apparently filled almost to the level of the ground around them.

Some astronomers had predicted meteorite craters on Mars, but the pictures were generally a surprise. Well over 70 craters were clearly pictured on about one per cent of the Martian surface, suggesting that the entire planet must have in excess of 10,000 craters within the same size range—to this degree, a surface reminiscent of the moon's. The surface of the airless, waterless moon is known to be extremely ancient, perhaps 2,000 to 4,500 million years old. It is as well preserved as it is because it has escaped wind and water erosion for all that time. If the Martian surface is similar, according to one early line of reasoning, it must be just as ancient. If it also shows no sign of water erosion, Mars can never have had much atmosphere or liquid water. Without them, so the story went, the planet is unlikely to have supported life at any time in its history.

This pessimistic conclusion was quickly challenged. Mars lives in a bad neighbourhood of the solar system, where flying rocks are a frequent hazard. Between its orbit and that of Jupiter lies the asteroid zone, where thousands of rocky and metallic bodies revolve round the sun. There are probably 50,000 asteroids big enough to be seen with large telescopes. Most of them stay in their proper zones, but a considerable number move in orbits taking them into other regions of the solar system.

Along with the visible asteroids move uncounted millions of meteorites too small to be seen but large enough to blast conspicuous craters in any planet they hit. The earth and moon have suffered many of these impacts and Mars, being closer to the asteroid belt, must have had many more. Fragments chipped off the asteroids in their collisions with each other must strike Mars and contribute to its cratered surface. It has been estimated that during any selected period Mars must have been hit by about 25 times as many meteorites as hit the moon. If the planet's surface were really ancient and free of significant erosion, it should be much more pitted than the moon's. Since it is not, erosion must be very effective on Mars and its surface must be younger than the moon's. Something must have eroded the ancient craters formed during Mars' youth, most likely water or wind. Though the planet has no oceans now and lacks a substantial atmosphere, it may have had both in the past and thus may have been more favourable for the development of life.

The controversy over Martian life was by no means settled when Mariners VI and VII passed close to Mars (within 2,131 miles and 2,130 miles respectively), or even when orbiting Mariner IX and the Russian craft zoomed within 800 miles of it twice a day. These vehicles transmitted to earth a wealth of highly detailed information. Much of the surface surveyed was indeed cratered, though none as thickly as the ancient "highlands" of the moon. But the big surprise was that Mars has large areas with few or no craters.

Perhaps most remarkable is a large, light-coloured area—visible from the earth and named Hellas—that proved almost featureless. It is apparently a plain 1,200 miles in diameter separated from a heavily cratered region by a narrow zone of valleys and ridges. It is not like the moon's comparatively smooth "seas", all of which are blemished with small craters.

On other parts of Mars the cratered surface changes suddenly to a craterless terrain of jumbled ridges. One picture shows what looks as if the roof of a great underground cave had fallen in to form a "slump valley". Its bottom is laced with thin lines that resemble cattle trails seen from an aeroplane. Surely no cattle graze in that Martian valley, but neither the "trails" nor the valley is easily explained, nor is the Martian equator's huge bulge, detected by Mariner IX.

New-found mysteries

As often happens in science, the clear pictures from the Mariner spacecraft raised more mysteries than they solved. In spite of its many craters, Mars is not like the moon. Neither is it like the earth, but some parts of its surface appear to be fresh and young and full of new-found mystery.

An old mystery remains also, as interesting as ever. None of the Mariners explained the "wave of darkening", the seasonal change that has been used to support the belief in some sort of Martian life. They passed the planet too quickly to observe slow changes of colour or darkness.

Mariner VII took excellent pictures of the white polar cap, which is not smooth and featureless like the earth's Antarctic ice cap. It shows cra-

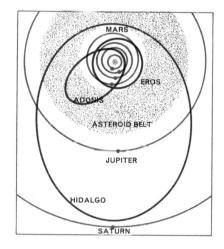

THE ASTEROID BELT, extending between Mars and Jupiter, was once thought to be composed of orbiting fragments of an exploded planet. Many astronomers now believe that the asteroids, sometimes called minor planets, are masses of rock and metal that might have formed another planet if they had not been jumbled by the effects of Jupiter's gravity. Most asteroids orbit within the belt; some, like Eros, Hidalgo and Adonis, travel unusual elongated paths.

ters and other irregularities and great, mysterious variations of brightness. Some ripple-like markings may be due to local clouds. The edge of the cap is ragged, with fine white details showing brightly against an adjacent darker zone. As might be expected, the crater slopes facing the sun have more "snow" than those in the shadow.

It is doubtful whether Martian snow is really crystallized water like the earth's snow. Mariner space craft have carried instruments to measure the temperature of the Martian surface. Near the equator the temperature rose to 15° or 25°C., but over the southern cap it fell to as low as −123°C. This is about the temperature of carbon dioxide freezing to crystals at the pressure of the Martian atmosphere. So the white caps of Mars may consist wholly or largely of dry ice (solid carbon dioxide).

A vanished ocean

The possibility that Mars may have supported life in the distant past depends on its early history, about which not much is known. Conjectures about it are necessarily vague. Soon after its formation, Mars, like all primitive planets, was presumably surrounded with a primordial atmosphere of "reducing" gases rich in hydrogen, such as ammonia and methane. At a later stage, unknown amounts of other gases, including water vapour, must have come out of its interior. If the Martian upper atmosphere was always at the relatively low temperatures it is believed to be at today, no gases except light-weight hydrogen could simply escape into space, as the moon's gases did. Mars is so far from the sun that the top of its atmosphere probably does not get hot enough to accelerate the heavier molecules to the needed escape velocity. What, then, happened to the gases?

A promising hypothesis to explain what became of the water vapour, at least, begins with a clue from Mariner IV. The space-craft's instruments reported that Mars has no detectable magnetic field. It may therefore lack an iron core, which may mean that the iron in the material from which Mars was formed did not sink towards the planet's centre. If the iron remained plentiful on and near the surface, it may have been the final cause of the water vapour's disappearance.

In the first step of this process, water vapour in the atmosphere is separated by solar ultra-violet light into oxygen and hydrogen. The hydrogen released quickly escapes into space. In the next step the oxygen combines with iron, forming a rust-like compound. This takes oxygen out of the atmosphere and keeps it from accumulating there. Therefore the Martian atmosphere never acquired enough oxygen to shield its remaining water from decomposition by ultra-violet light, as is the case on the earth. With liquid water gone from the surface, water vapour would become scarce in the atmosphere, reducing its effectiveness for holding heat. Mars would therefore get colder and turn into what it is today, an almost frozen planet with no free oxygen or open bodies of water and only a small, variable amount of water vapour above its surface.

The rust theory of Martian history is supported by observations. When sunlight is reflected from the surface of Mars, the light is altered in several ways by what it encounters there. The material found on the earth that alters light in the way that is most similar is limonite, an iron oxide chemically combined with water. It is dull orange-red and when finely pulverized has properties strikingly like the deserts of Mars.

The combined action of ultra-violet light and rusting iron may have been slow, so those who like to think that Mars was once more favourable for the appearance of life can look back hopefully to the youth of the planet. At that time it may have had a good deal of water on its surface and a climate warm enough to keep at least some water in the liquid state. If ammonia, methane and other reducing gases were present in its atmosphere, the stage would have been set, as it was on the earth, for the appearance of life.

Any kind of life that got a start on Mars would have slowly evolved by natural selection to keep up with changes in the environment. Life is enormously resourceful. If free oxygen were never present in the atmosphere, living things could thrive without it, as many of the earth's organisms do. If liquid water became scarce, Martian organisms might come to retain a supply in their tissues and add to that precious hoard by acquiring other forms of water from the environment.

Insects with anti-freeze

Living things are able to adapt themselves to extreme conditions. Many of the earth's micro-organisms, for example, can withstand almost any degree of cold while they are in a dormant state. Some insects winter-proof themselves with glycerol, a common anti-freeze used in car radiators. There is no conclusive reason why Martian organisms should not add so much anti-freeze to their tissues that they can live and reproduce in the extremely cold temperatures occurring on Mars.

More radical adaptations are possible, granted the origin of life on Mars and its subsequent evolution. If finely powdered limonite is an important constituent of Martian deserts, it may conceivably have become a medium of life. Each molecule of iron oxide in limonite is combined with about one water molecule. Any organisms that have found a way to extract water from limonite could live in the Martian deserts as if they were in oceans.

The possibility that Mars may support life is intensely interesting to scientists in fields outside astronomy. Many biologists feel that their science has potentially broader perspectives than the study of life on earth. On the biochemical level, all of the earth's multitudinous organisms have many more striking similarities than differences. All are believed to be descendants of a single remote ancestor whose basic chemistry they still retain. They all store the coded information that enables them to reproduce their species in large, coiled molecules of nucleic acid. They all use similar proteins (the enzymes) to promote and control the chemical processes that take place in their tissues. Not a single deviation from this general pattern has been found on the earth, though there are literally millions of closely related chemical compounds that might be used.

A SPIDER-LIKE MARTIAN, peering out of his space cylinder at an earthling in an illustration from H. G. Wells's *The War of the Worlds*, was the bizarre product of science wedded to fiction. Wells, writing in 1898, described his Martians as foundering under the strong gravitational pull of the earth, destroying everything in their path with a "heat ray" (a forerunner of the laser beam), and finally being wiped out by common bacteria, for which they had no defence.

Why this curious narrowness?, ask the biologists. They are eager to find out whether only one kind of life is possible or whether there may be others. Perhaps the earth's present type is the lone survivor of many less efficient kinds of life that appeared on the early earth and were eliminated by competition. Or perhaps it has survived and differentiated because it pre-empted the earth 4,000 million years ago and created conditions that kept competitors from gaining a foothold. During that distant age, the biologists muse, there must have come a critical time when only one example of the earth's kind of life was in existence. If this first ancestor —the original, primitive, microscopic Adam—had been killed by some misadventure, perhaps by an encounter with a cosmic ray, might all organisms living on the modern earth have had a different ancestor, different chemistry and a different appearance and behaviour?

The broad philosophical question of whether more than one kind of life is possible cannot be answered on the earth for a long time, if ever. Creation of complex forms of life in the laboratory appears to be far too difficult. But Mars may be a natural laboratory where life appeared thousands of millions of years ago and where descendants of those first organisms are still available for study. Only a few humble micro-organisms need be found to provide a second example of life. If they have the same chemistry as life on earth, and if we are sure biological contamination of Mars has not occurred, they will strengthen the view that only a single kind of life is possible. If they have some other chemical pattern, they will enlarge the horizons of biology. Life will be proved to be a far-ranging influence that can mould non-living matter in diverse, independent ways, some of which may be suited to conditions widely different from the earth's.

Micro-environments

The discovery of life on Mars would be an event of profound significance but the task of detecting it may not be easy. Orbiting cameras, however sharp-eyed, would almost certainly fail to spot micro-organisms that live below the surface. Martian life may be confined to special places, micro-environments, where living conditions are unusually favourable. There is a good chance that water exists frozen under the surface; the red deserts may conceivably be frozen oceans covered with dust. Since Mars must be hotter inside, the ice should turn to liquid water a moderate distance below the surface. If this is the case, any strong disturbance such as a volcanic eruption, meteorite impact or violent Marsquake may let water or water vapour escape, creating a moist "hot spot" especially suitable for life. An orbiting space craft equipped to measure temperature and water vapour might detect such micro-environments.

To go a step further and determine the nature of Martian life requires the landing of an unmanned vehicle on the surface of the planet. The first such probe, Mars 3, was set down by the Soviet Union in December 1971, but it fell silent after transmitting signals for less than an hour. A more elaborate scientific assault on the red planet is scheduled for the latter half of the decade, when the American Viking project begins. On the first mission, two capsules—equipped with seismometers, water detectors, cameras, magnets, devices to collect soil samples and instruments to conduct life-detection experiments—will soft-land at sites determined from Mariner IX and Russian space craft data. A vehicle orbiting overhead will carry instruments to survey the landing sites and analyse atmospheric conditions on Mars.

Full understanding of Martian life may have to wait until human biologists have landed on the planet and studied the different micro-environments. This will be a formidable job. Though Mars is smaller than the earth, its lack of oceans gives it about the same land area. The terrain is extremely varied. Besides numerous craters, Mars probably has extensive highlands that may correspond to the earth's continents. Radar astronomy shows that their highest points may rise as much as 12 miles above the low-lying deserts, and the Mariner photographs show many mysterious markings that have not been identified.

Exploration of Mars also includes investigation of its extraordinary satellites, Deimos and Phobos, whose small size and proximity to the planet make them unique in the solar system. Deimos is approximately three miles in diameter and about 15,000 miles from the surface of Mars. Phobos, five miles in diameter, is much closer (5,800 miles). Despite their small size, they were photographed by Mariner IX.

The most remarkable thing about Phobos, according to some observations, is that its period of revolution appears to be decreasing slowly but perceptibly. The only plausible explanation is that the slight drag of the Martian atmosphere is taking energy from it, thus making it move closer to Mars and follow a shorter and faster orbit. The Martian atmosphere is so thin that a satellite affected in this way must have extremely low density. If the observations are correct (which is not established), Phobos must be lighter than any known solid substance.

The strange satellite of Mars

The Russian astronomer Iosif S. Shklovsky has supplied a novel answer to this puzzle. He believes that Phobos is hollow and artificial, the work of highly civilized Martians of hundreds of millions of years ago. When they decided that they would soon become extinct, his reasoning continues, they constructed one or two extraordinarily spacious satellites to serve as libraries and museums and to preserve for future explorers the glorious history and achievements of their doomed civilization.

Few scientists (Shklovsky included) actually count on finding any such convenient repositories of ancient learning, and discovering any sort of intelligent, civilized life still flourishing is considered extremely unlikely. But explorers of Mars will certainly look for archaeological evidence of long-dead civilizations. The beginning of life on a planet and its evolution towards higher forms has no fixed time-table. Life may have started early on Mars and evolved faster, reaching its civilized climax hundreds of millions of years ago. Even if nothing nearly as spectacular is found on Mars, the exploration of the planet will be an event unmatched in history.

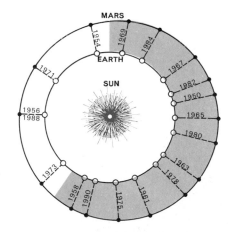

OPPOSITIONS OF MARS, which occur every 780 days when the earth passes between Mars and the sun, provide the best periods for viewing the planet. Due to the different shapes of the planets' orbits, some oppositions (*light area*) are better for observation than others. The most favourable oppositions occur during the month of August at 15- or 17-year intervals, when the earth and Mars are closest together, within 35 million miles of each other.

The Changing Image of Mars

Through the centuries, Mars has stirred men's imaginations as has no other planet. To the ancients, its reddish glow was a celestial symbol of blood, and Mars was long personified as a god of war (*opposite*). Persistent speculation that there might be intelligent beings on Mars reached extravagant proportions early in the 20th century after American astronomer Percival Lowell interpreted the markings on Mars, seen by several astronomers, as canals that were the product of a culture far in advance of earth's. In the following years, an entire Martian civilization, complete with a capital city on Solis Lacus ("Sun Lake") sprang from a host of fertile imaginations.

Today, most astronomers believe that canals do not exist on Mars, at least in the form depicted by Lowell. Nevertheless, most think that there may be some life forms on the red planet. They point to a change on Mars in spring, when the surface shades turn darker, as a phenomenon that may be evidence of life. Even if this belief is incorrect, there may be organisms on Mars able to survive extreme cold, dryness and lack of oxygen, as some earthly organisms do.

THE SYMBOL OF WAR
Mars, shown as an armour-clad god of war, in this 15th-century illustration, presides over the siege of an Italian city. The symbolic link between Mars and war was first made by the Sumerians in the third millennium B.C. and was continued by the Persians, Greeks and Romans. The astrological symbols of Scorpio and Aries mark the limit of the annual war-making season: March to October.

A Vision of Canals and Cities

The "discovery" of straight, geometrically patterned channels, or *canali*, on Mars by the Italian astronomer Giovanni Schiaparelli in 1877, and the subsequent conclusion by Percival Lowell that these were canals built by intelligent beings, touched off a controversy among astronomers at the turn of the century. Many, like the U.S.'s Edward E. Barnard, stoutly denied that any such lines even existed and implied that they were the result of overactive imaginations. Some claimed the *canali* were optical illusions that disintegrated into short, disconnected features when viewed during the clearest periods.

Modern astronomers dismiss Lowell's elaborate map of Martian canals (*opposite*). They admit that there may be lines on Mars (*page 145*) but conjecture that they probably mark ancient fractures in the crust or long rows of wind-whipped sand dunes.

A WORLD FROM A BLUR

The drawing above, by Giovanni Schiaparelli, reveals the vaguely defined lines he thought were of geologic origin, like the English Channel. Percival Lowell, using Schiaparelli's information and his place names, drew the 1903 map (*right*) which shows a complex of canals—some as wide as 50 miles—radiating out from oases and polar caps to connect Martian cities.

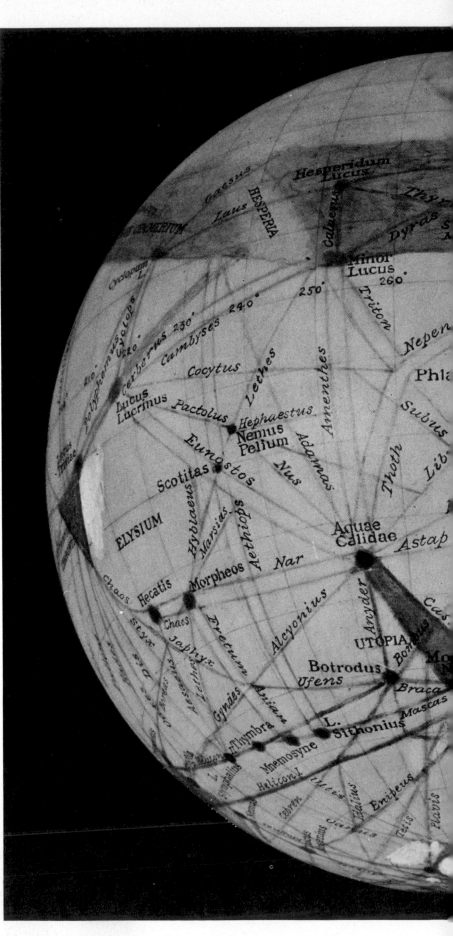

142

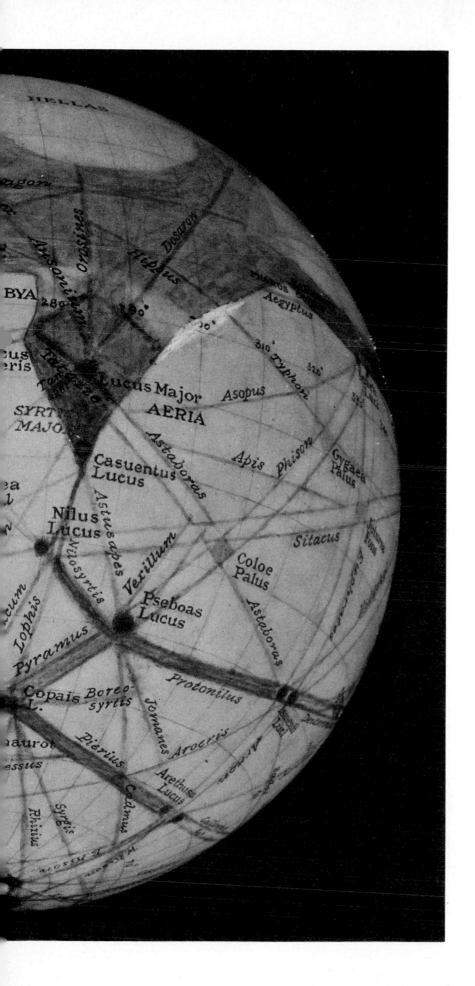

VENICE ON MARS
A lofty, glass-domed city, served by great waterways, is shown in this illustration of Lowell's concept. It was taken from a Russian film that discussed Lowell's hypothesis, as well as others.

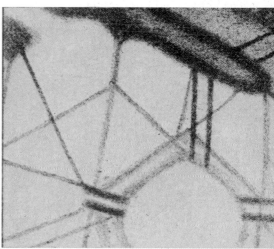

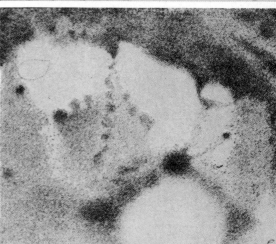

TWO VIEWS OF THE "CANALS"
The Schiaparelli map (*top*) shows a pattern of *canali*, many of them parallel, he described as being like "the finest thread of a spider's web". But astronomer Eugenios M. Antoniadi drew a different picture (*bottom*) after viewing the same area in moments of exceptional clarity. He saw indistinct patterns, the *canali* having dissolved into disjointed smudges on the surface.

Close Looks at an Unearthly Planet

The real face of Mars, a far different sight from any ever seen from earth, was first disclosed by the United States planet-probing robot space craft Mariner IV in 1965. After a trip of more than seven months and 325 million miles, it passed Mars at a distance of 6,100 miles and sent its photographs back to earth providing astronomers with invaluable clues to the planet's configuration.

Even more spectacular views —three of which are shown here —came from the next Mars expedition in 1969, when Mariner VI flew by on the 31st July, followed by Mariner VII 5 days later. Both made close passes at the planet, approaching it within some 2,130 miles to record temperature and analyse the Martian atmosphere. The Mariners found a cold, nearly airless, seemingly waterless planet, no evidence either for or against the existence of life and few signs of the maddeningly elusive canals. A total of 200 stunningly sharp pictures were sent back revealing heavily cratered areas, smooth and craterless plains, and a mysterious region of wild hills and chaotic valleys that prompted one scientist to comment: "Mars is really its own planet".

ZEROING IN ON MARS

From 293,200 miles away, Mariner VII reveals a jumble of bright patches and wiggly lines that change during the Martian day. The bright ring near the centre is Nix Olympicus, probably a giant crater. Two of the whitish patches below and to the right of it are parts of the mysterious "W" cloud, named after its shape. At the bottom is the brilliant sheet of frost that caps the south pole.

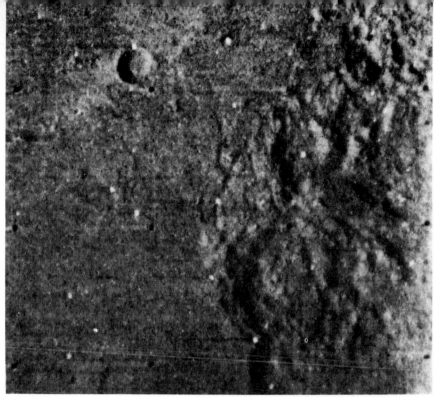

A CATACLYSMIC CAVE-IN

A smooth area on Mars abruptly yields to a region of wild, disorderly hills and valleys apparently below the ground level. Discovered by Mariner VI, this chaotic part of the planet is several hundred thousand square miles in area and unlike anything on the earth or the moon. One theory is that underground ice melted by local heat caused the collapse of huge caves.

CRATERS IN DEEP-FREEZE

Like footprints in the snow, craters reveal their outlines through the thin frost of Mars' south polar cap. Its temperature was gauged by Mariner VII as −123°C., close to the freezing point of carbon dioxide in the rarefied Martian atmosphere. This suggests that the polar ice on Mars is mostly powdery "dry ice", or frozen carbon dioxide, perhaps with traces of frozen water.

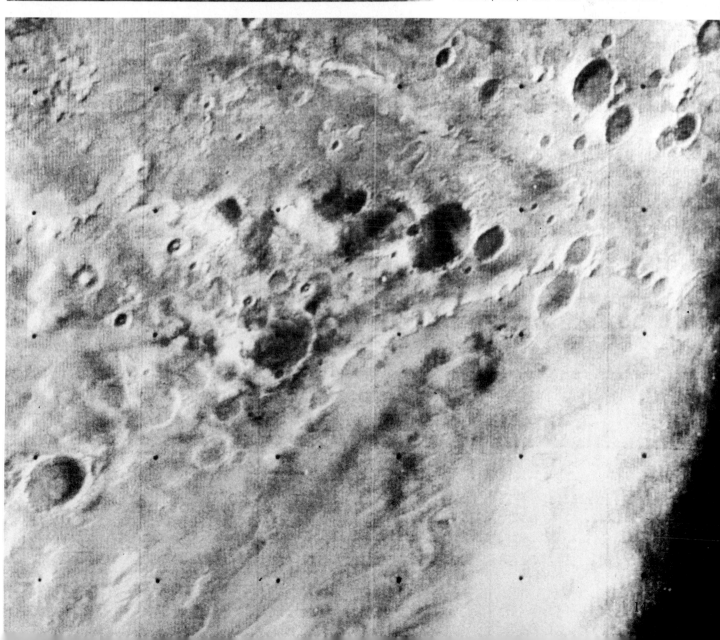

147

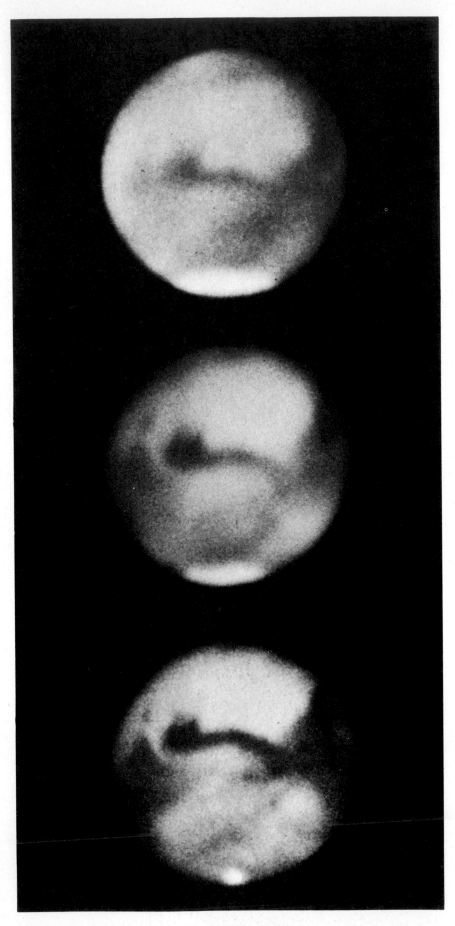

Three Faces of Mars

One thing on which all astronomers agree is that they can see Mars undergoing definite seasonal changes. As winter turns to spring, the polar frost cap recedes and a wave of darkening spreads from the pole towards the equatorial belt, as the telescopic photographs on the left illustrate. But what conclusions can be drawn from this phenomenon remains a matter of dispute. Some astronomers see the darkening landscape as evidence of awakening life: tiny organisms consuming water vapour released by the melting frost. Others insist that the Martian spring reveals nothing about life; the areas of darkness may be caused solely by seasonal winds which redistribute the fine particles of dust. Such problems of interpretation cannot be resolved as long as astronomers are restricted to their present equipment and techniques. Even a uniform description of Mars's springtime colours is difficult, as can be judged from the maps on the right.

SPRING COMES TO MARS
Three photographs trace the changes on the surface of Mars from late winter (*top*) through spring (*centre*) and into early summer (*bottom*). The polar frost cap can be seen as a shrinking circle at the bottom of each picture, while the dark areas become much more pronounced.

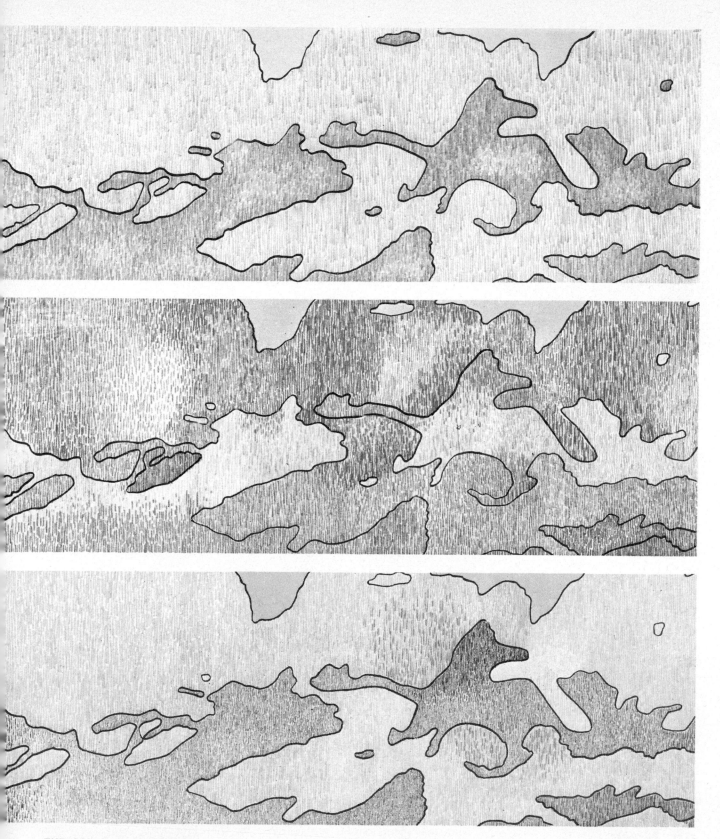

THE COLOURS OF SPRING

The difficulty in rendering the changing hues of a Martian spring is attested by these three maps of Mars's southern hemisphere, coloured from descriptions given by three different astronomers: Percival Lowell (*top*), Eugenios M. Antoniadi (*centre*) and Gerard P. Kuiper (*bottom*).

Such varying views show the tricks that Mars can play even on highly trained eyes. The human eye is an imperfect and unreliable instrument when it sees colours. It frequently attributes spurious colour to a neutral area that is next to a bright one. In addition, the colours the

astronomer sees may be distorted by the glass of his lens. Scientists now believe that the top two versions are inaccurate. But Kuiper, who used a different viewing technique, is close to the present consensus: burnt orange and grey, with some traces of brown and green.

Signs of Life on Mars

Many astronomers believe the changing tones that mark springtime on Mars may mean that life exists there. Just as sprouting plants provide the green colour of spring on earth, tiny organisms, perhaps the size of algae, are thought to be responsible for the darkening that characterizes the Martian season. According to this con-

cept, the organisms live just beneath the dusty surface. In the frigid winter they hibernate, using the water stored in their systems. But during the spring thaw, these organisms can absorb water from the surface or "drink" water vapour from the atmosphere. It is the mass movement towards the surface, where the organ-

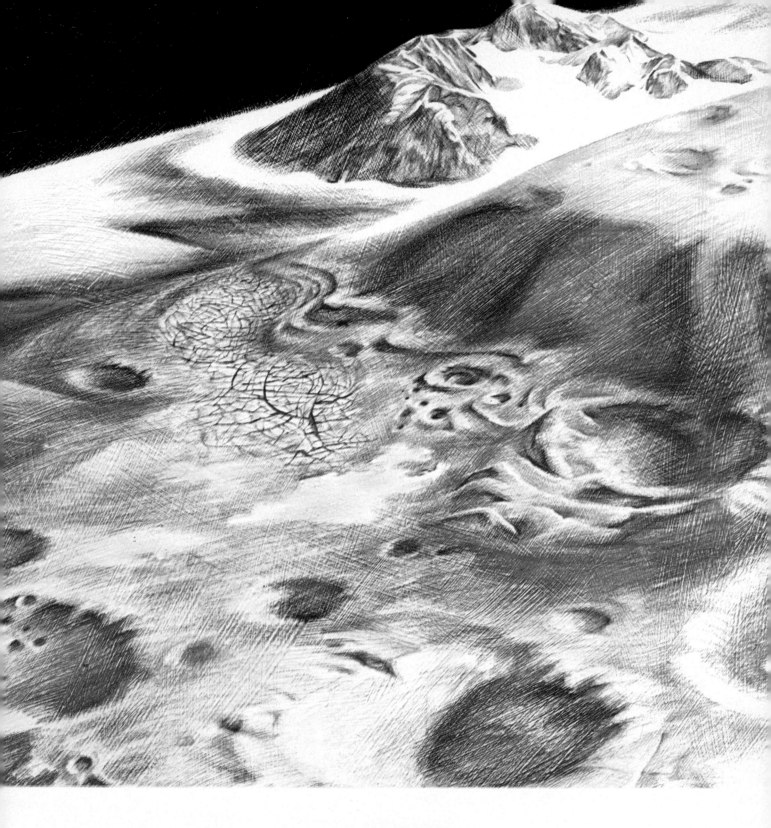

isms grow and multiply, that is said to cause the visible darkening.

This rendering of spring in a Martian polar region combines several biological hypotheses. The dark greygreen areas are the inhabited lowlands. Moisture comes from the frostcovered peaks at the upper right (in this view the frost is heaviest on the lower slopes, but other concepts place the thickest cover higher up). The frost yields water vapour to a spreading darker zone, in effect a breeding ground for colonies of the organisms (pink shading). A dry river-bed indicates that water has flowed on Mars, and a different form of aquatic life may exist in near-by brackish pools.

149

A Wind-swept Wasteland

A Martian spring has another explanation, according to some astronomers. They theorize that the springtime contrasts are the result of nothing more than wind sweeping fine specks of dust off the plateaux and into the lowlands. Because the larger particles remaining on the plateaux reflect less light, they appear darker to the observer on earth. In the autumn, the wind pattern is said to reverse, blowing the smaller particles back on to the plateaux and restoring the contrasts upon the Martian surface once more.

Even though the seasonal changes are not due to life in this theory, there still may be life present that cannot be seen.

The grey-green plateaux are studded with craters eroded by wind—but not rain. Clouds of dust swirl through the valley, occasionally twisting into a tornado-like dust devil (*upper left*).

But not until scientists can get a close-up look will it be possible to make a more conclusive assessment of whether Mars is or is not a planet harbouring life. This will be the main objective of Project Viking, the United States' effort to land an unmanned laboratory on Mars in the 1970's.

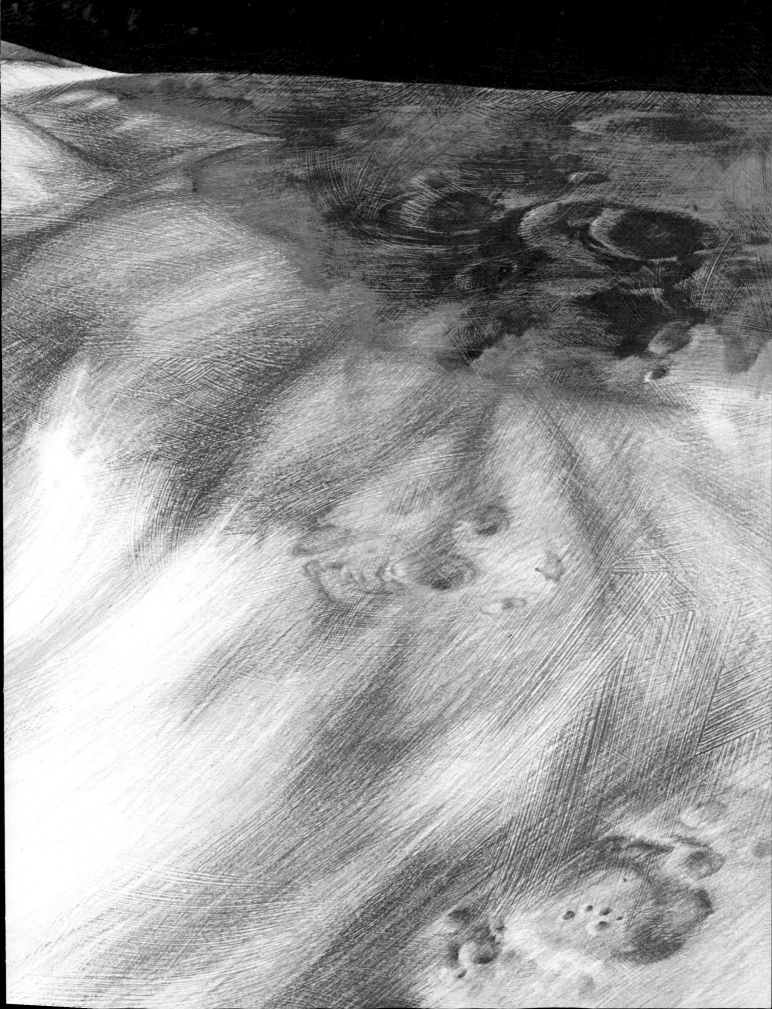

7

A Strange
Veiled
Giant

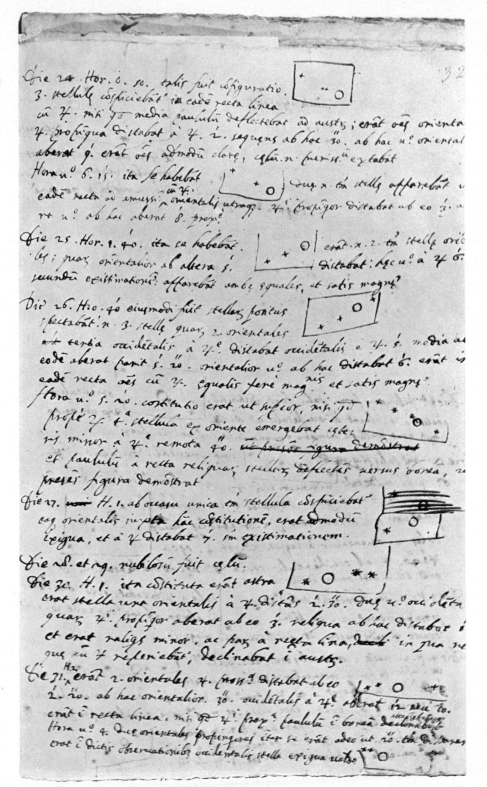

Galileo's words and sketches record his discovery of four of Jupiter's satellites in 1610.

JUPITER, THE LARGEST PLANET, is also the liveliest. It rotates in less than 10 hours, faster than any other planet. Its markings sweep across its face in a single evening, and a sharp eye at a good telescope can see distinct changes in a few minutes. It is hard to remember while watching these rapid motions how enormous Jupiter is. If Mars were placed on the face of Jupiter, it would look like a sixpence on a dinner plate. Jupiter has more than 11 times the earth's diameter, 300 times the mass and 1,000 times the volume. It has 12 satellites, more than any other planet, and it contains twice as much matter as all the other planets put together. In some respects it may behave more like a star than a planet of the solar system.

Jupiter is not only large but bizarre, full of violence, mysteries and surprises. Its highest clouds are chiefly ammonia snow-flakes. Its turbulent atmosphere reaches thousands of miles deep, so deep that no one knows where it ends. In nearly every way Jupiter is utterly unlike the earth. Its extreme temperatures, its prodigious pressures and its atmosphere poisonous to man would seem to make it uninhabitable, but this negative judgement is now known to be unjustified. Recent work on the origin of life and the environment of Jupiter suggests that it may be more favourable to life than any other planet, not excepting the earth.

The first step towards understanding Jupiter is to note that although its mass is enormous, the planet is not dense. In fact, its density is remarkably low, only 1.33 times that of water. The earth is about 4.1 times as dense, about like iron ore. The surprisingly low density of Jupiter is the key to its composition. There is only one substance that could keep such low density despite the compression of Jupiter's powerful gravitation, and that substance is hydrogen, the lightest of all the elements. If it were mixed with 10 per cent or so of helium, the second-lightest element, the combination under compression would approximate the density of Jupiter. Heavier elements such as those that make up most of the earth cannot be present in large proportions. Spectroscopic and other evidence supports this conclusion by showing that the atmosphere of Jupiter is indeed largely hydrogen and helium.

The hydrogen-helium combination has a clear meaning for astronomers. These light gases are comparatively rare on the earth, but they are by far the commonest elements in the stars and interstellar matter that form the bulk of the universe. Their abundance in Jupiter shows that the planet has changed comparatively little in composition since the solar system condensed out of interstellar gas and dust 5,000 million years ago. In Jupiter's central core or mixed throughout its interior may be enough iron, silicon and other heavy elements to make a dense planet about the size of the earth, but these materials are overwhelmed by hydrogen and helium. As a result, Jupiter is more like the sun in composition than it is like the earth.

While all planets were probably formed initially from a hydrogen-rich mixture of gases, the earth and its near neighbours have lost almost all their initial atmospheres. Jupiter has retained hydrogen and helium because of its large gravitation and its distance from the sun. In its remote orbit, 486 million miles from the sun, sunlight is only $1/27$ as strong as it is on the earth. The planet's outer atmosphere is so cold that hardly any hydrogen molecules get moving fast enough to escape from the powerful gravitation. But if the sun ever grows much brighter, as astronomers believe it eventually will, Jupiter's exterior temperature may rise enough to permit the departure of first hydrogen, then helium. If this happens, the planet will shrink to a small, dense globe of heavy elements, somewhat like the earth.

The knowledge that Jupiter's huge mass is composed almost entirely of hydrogen and helium gives astronomers something to start with in devising a model of the planet. Even the comparatively light atmospheric gases of Jupiter are powerfully compressed by their own weight, because the great gravitation—at cloud-top level it is 2.6 times as strong as the earth's—makes everything correspondingly heavy. A few thousand miles below the visible cloud deck the pressure is so enormous that the hydrogen becomes thick, and at some point farther down it probably turns to a kind of solid. Whether Jupiter has a sharply defined surface is uncertain. The main mass of solid hydrogen may be covered with a slush composed of fluid hydrogen mixed with particles of materials that solidify more readily than hydrogen does.

Where hydrogen becomes a metal

Even farther down, no one knows just how far, an extraordinary change is believed to take place as the hydrogen is subjected to tremendous compression. When pressure rises above a million earth atmospheres (one atmosphere equals 14.7 pounds per square inch), hydrogen atoms are crushed in such a way that their electrons are separated from their nuclei. In this state hydrogen behaves like a metal. It is denser than normal solid hydrogen and like most metals is a good conductor of electricity. Jupiter's core is believed to be made of this strange stuff—a metallic version of an element known on earth as the lightest of all gases.

Jupiter's atmosphere is as remarkable as its core. The surface of the clouds—which is all that is visible of the planet—has been studied for centuries. Even a small telescope shows the numerous, quickly changing markings that make Jupiter unique. Parallel to its equator, covering most of the surface, run alternate bright and dark bands. About 10 are generally visible, but 14 appear often enough to have been named. Dark bands are called "belts", while bright bands are "zones", such as the "North Tropical Zone". The belts and zones continually shift, merge, fade, or grow wider or narrower. Bright or dark patches appear suddenly in them, spread out into streaks and disappear.

Astronomers had hardly begun to study Jupiter when they found that its visible surface does not rotate as a unit. The bands within 10 degrees of the equator complete a rotation about five minutes faster than the bands to the south and north of them, one group racing past the other at about 220 m.p.h. These racing parallel bands are easy to explain in a general way; the earth has something like them. The earth's trade winds, which blow from east to west, and its prevailing westerlies, which blow from west to east, are currents of air originally set in motion by the solar heating at the equator. On a non-rotating earth, some of these currents would blow northwards and others southwards, but the earth's rotation turns them into west or east winds. If these currents could be identified by the colour of their clouds and were not disturbed by ground topography, they would look from space rather like Jupiter's bands. Since Jupiter is much larger than the earth, it would be only natural that it should have more "trade winds" and "prevailing westerlies" than the earth has.

Except for these east-west currents, the atmosphere of Jupiter does not resemble the earth's. It has no detectable oxygen or nitrogen, the gases that make up the bulk of the earth's atmosphere, but spectroscopy has determined that it has ammonia and methane along with the predominant hydrogen and helium. Scientists infer that water vapour is also present. They reason that an assortment of elements typical of the universe at large contains oxygen, and on Jupiter it must have combined with hydrogen to form water.

Snow and rain made of ammonia

The conspicuous clouds in Jupiter's bright bands are probably not composed of water. These are indicated by spectroscopic evidence and temperature measurements to be ammonia crystals hanging high in the atmosphere, where the pressure is about five times the earth's at sea level and the temperature is low enough to keep solid ammonia from evaporating. Below the ammonia crystal clouds are probably clouds of liquid ammonia droplets. Still farther down, water vapour condenses as ice crystals, and below that water droplets. All these crystals and droplets fall, so Jupiter must have ammonia snow and ammonia rain, and water snow and water rain. None of this precipitation falls very far; it evaporates a little below the clouds and the vapour is carried up to the clouds again. This meteorological turmoil, which is much more violent than any weather on the earth, is almost certainly accompanied by enormous electrical discharges that would make earthly strokes of lightning look like harmless sparks.

In the midst of this maelstrom stands the most stable—and perhaps the most unusual—visible feature on Jupiter: the Great Red Spot. It is a long oval area set into the South Tropical Zone at a latitude equivalent to Rio de Janeiro on earth. Its size has varied somewhat but it is usually 8,000 miles broad and 25,000 miles long, which is more than three times the earth's diameter. The colour of the Spot varies; it is sometimes brick red, sometimes dull pink, sometimes grey. It has a rotational speed of its own, moving four and a half miles per hour slower than the brighter material around it. Sometimes it seems to disappear entirely, showing its presence by an indentation, the Red Spot Hollow, in the adjacent South Equatorial Belt.

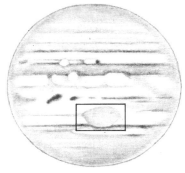

JUPITER'S GREAT RED SPOT (*in box above*) is its most prominent feature. Although its erratic movements and changing shape and colour (*below*) have been observed since the 19th century, there is still no completely satisfactory theory to account for its origin. Astronomers are not even sure what gives it its colour, although both visual and spectroscopic observations have proved that the Great Red Spot is indeed red much of the time.

1882

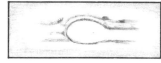

1921

1923

1938

What this gigantic discoloration might be has puzzled astronomers for centuries. Until recently the Spot was considered some sort of solid object floating in the dense lower atmosphere and showing its upper surface above the clouds. One objection to this explanation is that no known solid substance is light enough to float in the hydrogen-rich atmosphere of Jupiter no matter how strongly compressed. Another is that any free-floating body subjected to the rotational forces of rapidly spinning Jupiter would drift towards the equator, and in 300 years the Great Red Spot has shown no sign of such drifting.

The most widely accepted modern theory holds that the Spot is caused by a topographical feature, either a rise or a depression, on Jupiter's solid hydrogen "surface". The feature must be very large, but it need be no more than a few miles high or deep. Influenced by the planet's rotation, the dense atmosphere flows around the feature, and generates a column of relatively stagnant gas—called a Taylor column—that extends upwards. The column reaches through the tops of the bright ammonia clouds, where it shows as the Great Red Spot.

The origin of the topographical feature that apparently causes the Great Red Spot is not known, but there are several promising possibilities. Jupiter's interior may be in motion like the earth's mantle, wrinkling the surface into mountain ranges of solid hydrogen, one of which is large enough to cause the Spot. Another possibility is that something outside Jupiter—such as a large comet or asteroid—may have scarred the surface. Or perhaps a heat source below the surface turns large amounts of solid hydrogen to gas, thus creating a depression big enough to support a Taylor column.

The planet that acts like a star

Jupiter does seem to be generating some heat of its own. Delicate recent measurements of its temperature suggest that it gives off about twice as much energy as it acquires from the sun. It may, indeed, be acting as an exceedingly feeble star. The sun was once feeble, too. When it began to form out of a thin cloud of interstellar gas and dust, its centre was comparatively cool, but as it collected more material from outside, its mass increased and so did the strength of its gravitation. The increased pull made the great ball of gas contract, and the contraction (equivalent to falling towards the centre) released gravitational energy that turned into heat. Not until the sun's centre reached the temperature of many millions of degrees did thermonuclear reactions start and make it shine as a true star.

Since Jupiter's interior is not hot enough to sustain the thermonuclear reactions that power full-grown stars like the sun, the most likely source of its excess heat energy is contraction. Jupiter may be shrinking as the sun once did, its material falling slowly towards the centre and releasing gravitational energy that appears as heat. In some unknown manner the heat works its way to the surface, where it stirs the atmosphere to turbulence and motion and makes it radiate into space a little more energy than it receives from the sun.

Not all astronomers accept this chain of reasoning. The heat that appears to flow from Jupiter's interior may be due to other causes. In any case, Jupiter is not a real star, and is not likely to get much hotter. But if its mass were 5 to 10 times as great, its increased gravitation would make it shrink to a smaller size, and its centre would get hot enough for thermonuclear reactions to start. Then Jupiter would shine with its own light as a "red dwarf" star, and the sun would be a double star like the thousands of millions of others in the sky.

Jupiter's big surprise

Whether Jupiter is an undersized star or an oversized planet, it behaves in remarkable ways, not the least surprising of which is its extraordinary activity in broadcasting radio waves. In 1955, when radio astronomy was still comparatively new, a telescope near Washington, D.C., was searching the sky for small new radio sources. The telescope picked up strong 22.2 megacycle (13.5 metre) waves that were at first attributed to ground interference such as cars with faulty ignition systems. The interference persisted, and although Jupiter was shining bright and high overhead at the time, none of the astronomers thought for several months of blaming it for the mysterious waves. At that time planets were not considered promising radio sources.

But the astronomers persisted and, to their great surprise, found that the source moved against the background of stars in a way that showed it must be Jupiter, which proved to be one of the strongest radio sources in the sky. Some of the waves have been traced to their origin on the planet; others are still mysterious, and the intricate puzzle they present makes Jupiter a favourite subject for radio astronomers.

The shortest of them, less than one inch long, come from above the clouds of Jupiter and give a temperature of −140° C., which is close to the temperatures obtained from infra-red studies. The slightly longer microwaves from Jupiter cannot come from the atmosphere or clouds, which would have to be absurdly hot to emit them as strongly as observed. Radio telescopes have shown that they originate in a huge region around Jupiter—a region 3.5 times the planet's diameter and completely outside the planet itself.

This finding confirmed an earlier suspicion that the microwaves must be generated by a gigantic belt that is analogous to the earth's Van Allen belts but is much, much larger. The particles themselves come from the sun, and they can be trapped in the belt only by a magnetic field. If Jupiter has a magnetic field, it would presumably arise from the electrically conducting core of metallic hydrogen, which would generate magnetism in somewhat the same way as the earth's core of metallic iron. No other planets are known to be like this. Neither Venus nor Mars nor the moon exhibits detectable magnetism and this lack has been taken to mean that none of them possesses a metal core.

The microwaves from Jupiter, informative though they may be, are

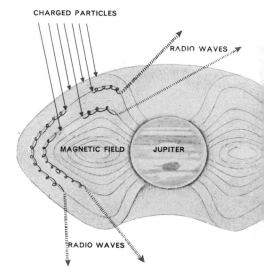

CHARGED PARTICLES

RADIO WAVES

MAGNETIC FIELD   JUPITER

RADIO WAVES

RADIO WAVES FROM JUPITER puzzled astronomers until radio telescopes revealed that they were not emitted by the planet itself but by particles trapped in its magnetic field (*elongated circles*). In a process analogous to the formation of the earth's Van Allen belts, charged particles from the sun (*arrows*) are trapped by Jupiter's magnetism. They then spiral around the planet, radiating waves directly in front of them that are powerful enough to be detected by receivers on earth, about 400 million miles distant from Jupiter.

not really so spectacular as the planet's longer, decametre waves. These waves, between 25 and 200 feet long, are almost incredibly powerful. They come in "bursts" and "storms", the bursts lasting anywhere from one-thousandth of a second to several seconds and the storms—each made up of a great many bursts—lasting as long as two hours. A single one-second burst releases radio waves equivalent in energy to those generated by 100,000 million earthly strokes of lightning. During a storm these enormous bursts follow one another in staccato succession, giving Jupiter a radio voice that must reach far beyond the solar system.

The powerful and capricious decametre waves baffled radio astronomers for quite a while. Their origin is still not entirely clear, but they are believed to come from charged particles of exceptionally high energy in Jupiter's belt. If these energetic particles stayed in the belt and circulated there in an orderly manner, they would not generate the tremendous bursts of decametre waves. But, like most things on Jupiter, they do not remain orderly. At irregular intervals great swarms of them plunge from the belt and down to the top of Jupiter's atmosphere, where they stop suddenly and expend part of their energy as radio waves. Scientists call this "dumping". Something similar happens when high-speed particles leave the earth's radiation belts and hit its atmosphere near the magnetic poles, causing the aurora, including the familiar northern lights. The frequent flickering of the aurora can be compared to the quickly repeated bursts of Jupiter's decametre waves.

Triggering the radio storms

It is not perfectly understood why Jupiter's storms of radio bursts should come at such irregular intervals. There are probably several triggering mechanisms that cause this dumping, but only one of them has been discovered so far. Storms of decametre waves are unusually frequent when Jupiter's nearest major satellite, Io, is at certain positions on its orbit, suggesting that the satellite triggers them. How does Io do this? A hint that may lead to a full explanation lies in the fact that the earth's moon leaves a sort of magnetic wake behind it. As the moon moves in its orbit, it sweeps up charged particles from the sun. Io is about as large as the moon, and its orbit carries it through Jupiter's magnetic field. It may somehow interfere with the free movement of the charged particles that are circulating there and cause them to be dumped into Jupiter's atmosphere.

Many mysteries still remain about Jupiter's radio waves. They seem to be almost as complicated as the sound waves emitted by an orchestra, and they are obviously full of hidden meanings. When they have been decoded they should answer many questions about giant Jupiter. They may tell, for instance, what parts of Jupiter have temperatures suitable for living organisms.

It might seem preposterous to suggest that life could survive on such a hostile planet, but Jupiter may be a good place for some forms of life to develop and evolve. In fact, conditions on present-day Jupiter are not

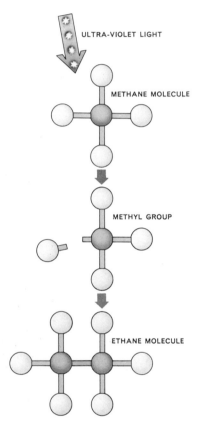

ORGANIC MOLECULES on Jupiter may be formed by a sequence like the one shown here. When ultra-violet light (*top*) charges a methane molecule with energy, one of its four hydrogen atoms is snapped off and the molecule becomes a methyl group. Two such groups can then join to form a complex molecule, ethane (*bottom*). Astronomers believe that similar reactions on Jupiter have produced even more complex molecules which may account for the bright colours of the planet's clouds, and may even have provided the basis for some form of life there.

ULTRA-VIOLET LIGHT

METHANE MOLECULE

METHYL GROUP

ETHANE MOLECULE

very far from those that apparently did produce life on the earth some 4,000 million years ago.

When the earth was first formed, its primordial atmosphere may not have been as extensive as Jupiter's, but it is believed to have contained the same essential gases. These are hydrogen, water vapour, ammonia and methane. All these gases are present in the atmosphere of Jupiter and it almost surely contains enough of the other elements—such as iron and phosphorus—that earthly life needs in small amounts.

The only other requirement for the appearance of complex organic compounds that are the precursors of life is a source of energy to break up simple molecules such as water and methane so that their fragments can join together. In the case of the earth, this energy source was probably ultra-violet light from the sun. If the sunlight on Jupiter is not sufficient, that planet probably has another source of energy: powerful lightning flashes in its turbulent and cloudy atmosphere. Laboratory experiments have proved that electric sparks—and strokes of lightning are nothing but large sparks—discharged through Jupiter-like mixtures of gases can produce complex organic molecules.

Where life might be found

Life could hardly begin in the tops of Jupiter's clouds, which are probably too cold, or in the bottom of its atmosphere, which is certainly too hot. But between the extremes there must be levels where water exists as liquid droplets. This is Jupiter's potential "life zone". Some adverse circumstances may have kept it free of life, but there is a chance that during the 5,000 million years of Jupiter's existence a combination of organic molecules may have acquired the critical ability to reproduce itself and evolve to higher forms.

That at least a part of this process has taken place is suggested by the positive colours of Jupiter's wind bands and of its Great Red Spot. The gases known to be abundant in Jupiter's atmosphere are essentially colourless, and the only coloured molecules that they can form are organic. Life and its chemical precursors can have any colour, from the green of a leaf to the red of blood. Great telescopes of the future, floating in space, may prove that Jupiter's Great Red Spot, like the earth's Red Sea, gets its colour from complex organic compounds.

If life has evolved on Jupiter, it will not be like familiar earthly life. Its basic chemistry may be wholly different, and in any case it will not breathe free oxygen because Jupiter's atmosphere has none. Since no solid surface is accessible, the organisms will have to float and, if large, they will have to be living balloons floating in gas. Most of them probably will be microscopic, but a few of them could be fairly large and could be equipped with some sort of propulsion to take them to their food. The chance that they will be intelligent is not considered good, but if life of any kind is found on Jupiter, it will show that life is possible on planets unlike the modern earth. It will strengthen the growing belief that life is a normal phenomenon throughout the universe.

Stormy Jupiter

Four hundred million miles from earth is a hulking giant of a planet, with a mass more than twice that of all the eight other planets put together. As it ponderously circles the sun once every 12 earth years, it drags along a dozen satellites. Its clouded atmosphere—which may harbour a violent realm of torrential ammonia rains and titanic blizzards—is striped by vast, shifting, multicoloured bands. These bands are not this planet's only markings. It has one of the most mysterious blemishes on the face of any planet: the Great Red Spot that comes and goes unpredictably, and is as wide as the earth. What lies beneath this decorated atmosphere may never be seen, because the pressure it exerts would crumple an exploring space ship like tin foil. The best guess is that the interior is mostly hydrogen, forced into a liquid or solid state—or both—by the pressures of the gases above it.

This planet is Jupiter, which seems to act as no true planet should. There is some evidence that Jupiter loses by radiation more heat energy than it acquires from the sun, and therefore it may be producing energy of its own—an activity ordinarily more characteristic of a star than of a planet.

JUPITER AND EARTH
The belts of frosty clouds that top Jupiter's atmosphere show up orange and grey in this telescopic photograph in contrast with the marking at the lower right, the Great Red Spot. This puzzling blot ranges in coloration from brick red to dull grey. The sun's largest planet, Jupiter is matched here to a scale representation of the earth, whose diameter is less than one-eleventh of Jupiter's.

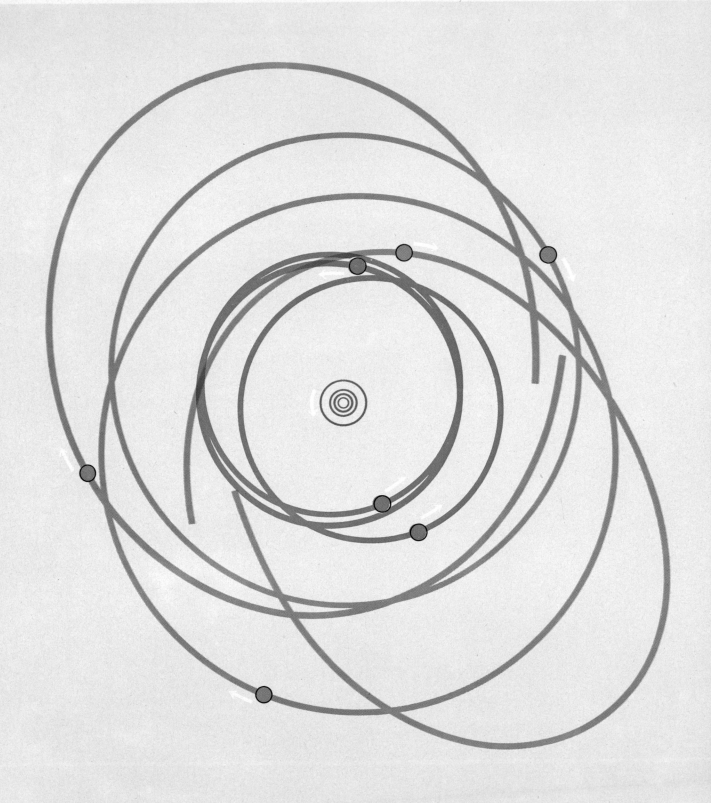

MOONS IN ALL DIRECTIONS

Jupiter's satellites trace a varied pattern of orbits. The four inner moons (*red*) provide a centre-piece of almost circular orbits, the farthest about a million miles out; a fifth inner satellite circles too close to Jupiter to be shown. Three other satellites (*purple*) orbiting about seven million miles out also have fairly circular paths. But the four outer satellites (*brown*) travel elongated paths in the "retrograde", or opposite, direction from the other eight; furthermore, two of these outer satellites have "open" orbits that are never repeated from one circuit to the next.

A Swarm
of Satellites

Jupiter's 12 satellites (two more than its nearest rival, Saturn) are every bit as remarkable as their parent planet. While most of them move in nearly perfect circles round the planet, a few make very elongated orbits. The inner eight orbit in the same direction in which the planet rotates, but the other four travel in the opposite direction from the others. These outer satellites are tiny, their average diameter probably less than 10 miles. They are so distant from Jupiter—about 14 million miles—that their behaviour is markedly affected by the sun's gravitational pull, which makes their orbits uncertain. Some scientists think they are really just asteroids forced out of their former orbits between Mars and Jupiter by

a gravitational tug-of-war won by Jupiter over the sun. Because they are small the outer satellites are very difficult to see. The last-discovered of these, which shines no brighter than the light of a candle seen from 3,000 miles away, was found only in 1951.

Jupiter's biggest, brightest moons are called Galilean satellites, after their discoverer. In size they loom over the outer satellites like beach balls over grains of sand.

The innermost satellite, known as V, is only 112,000 miles from Jupiter (about half the distance from the earth to its moon) and is about 70 miles in diameter. Jupiter's gravitational force causes tiny V to hurtle through space at 1,000 miles a minute, 26 times as fast as the earth's moon.

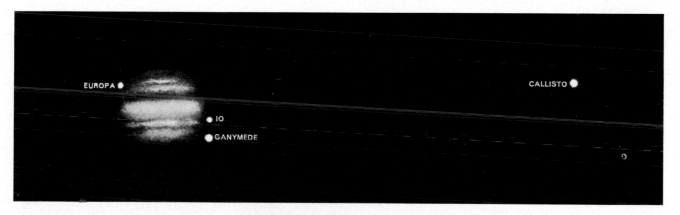

THE FOUR BRIGHTEST

The four Galilean satellites circle comparatively close to Jupiter, although one, Callisto (*right*), is more than a million miles away. The other three orbit in paths from 262,000 miles to 665,000 miles out. All four reflect light better than the earth's moon and two may have surfaces partially covered with an icy mixture of ammonia, nitrogen, carbon dioxide and water.

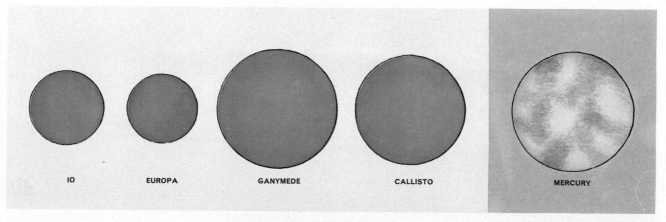

IO   EUROPA   GANYMEDE   CALLISTO   MERCURY

PLANET-SIZED MOONS

The Galilean satellites are so enormous that one of them, Ganymede, is actually 90 miles greater in diameter than the smallest planet, Mercury, as is shown in these scale drawings. Gany-

mede's diameter is 3,120 miles, while Mercury's is 3,030 miles. Callisto is next largest, measuring 2,770 miles, followed by Io and Europa with diameters of 2,020 and 1,790 miles.

The Mysterious Great Red Spot

Jupiter's heavily clouded atmosphere is believed to be a raging mass of ammonia hail and earth-like snow. But riding tranquilly amid all this turbulence is one of the most unusual features in the solar system, the Great Red Spot. This is a giant oval marking, up to 30,000 miles long and 8,000 miles wide, that moves slowly in relation to its immediately surrounding clouds, but always remains in Jupiter's South Tropical Zone. It drifts within the zone, often changes colour, and sometimes it disappears from view for years at a time.

Observed regularly since the late 19th century, the Spot has been explained in many ways: as a result of volcanic emissions, as an island in the atmosphere, and even as another moon in the process of being formed.

A widely discussed theory, illustrated here, has been advanced by Raymond Hide, formerly of the Massachusetts Institute of Technology. Hide believes that there must be a topographical irregularity on the surface of the planet, either an elevation or a depression. The rapid rotation of Jupiter prevents the flow of moving gases over this irregularity, forcing them to pass around it. This creates a tall column of relatively stagnant gas that rises through the atmosphere. The top of this column is seen as the Spot. When the Spot seems to disappear it is really still there. But for some reason its colour has changed to dull grey, which makes it blend with the outermost layer of clouds.

Jupiter's Great Red Spot appears at the top of a gauze-like column of gas in this illustration of Hide's theory. The gas column rises above

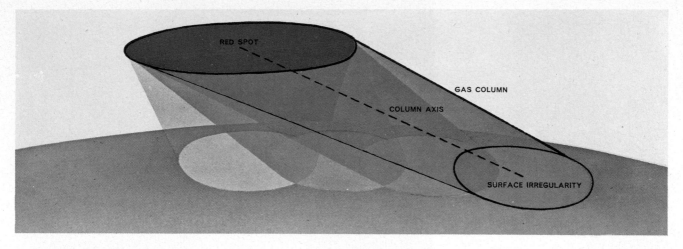

A WANDERING COLUMN

The location of the Spot in Jupiter's atmosphere does not necessarily pin-point the surface irregularity that causes it. The irregularity could be directly underneath the Spot or it could be out to one side, depending upon how the column of gas is inclined in relation to the surface. When the column is slanted at an extreme angle, the line from the feature to Spot (*dotted line*) is parallel to the axis of Jupiter's rotation.

some sort of unusual feature on the planet's surface. The atmosphere's clouds, which are actually opaque, are rendered as transparent here.

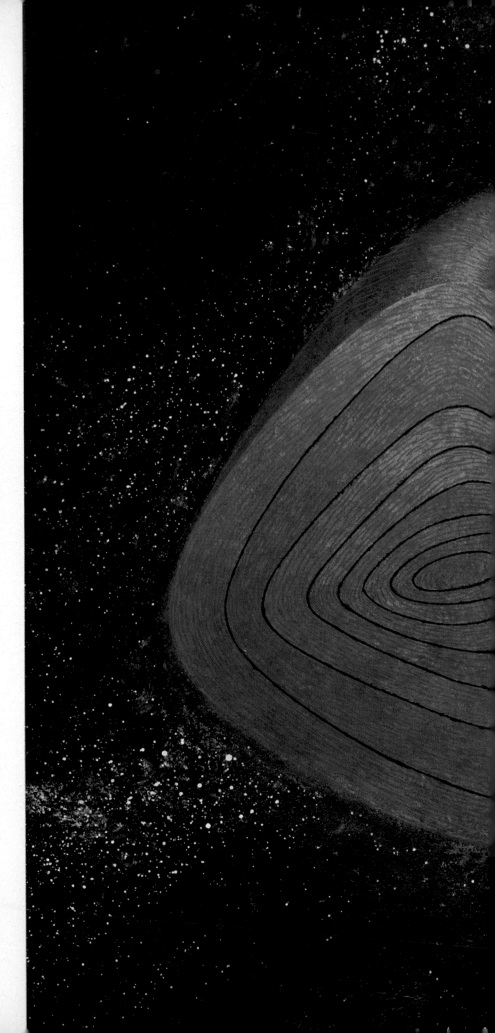

Outside Clues to What's Inside

One of the most revealing recent discoveries about Jupiter is that, like the earth, it has a powerful magnetic field. This is indicated by a vast, doughnut-shaped belt of electrically charged particles that encircles the planet—a ring similar to the Van Allen belts of charged solar particles held prisoner by the earth's magnetic field. Only the earth and Jupiter are known to have these belts, and some astronomers now reason that Jupiter, like the earth, must have a metallic core which acts like an electric generator to create a magnetic field. Since Jupiter is composed largely of hydrogen, the core may be mainly a solid form of hydrogen compressed and heated into a metallic state.

But what lies between core and atmosphere? Some scientists believe that there is an actual surface—a wrapper of rocks and ices. But most agree that the transition from solid core to gaseous atmosphere is gradual and that there is no discernible boundary; the internal pressures imposed by the planet's great mass are so enormous that the hydrogen of the atmosphere is eventually squeezed into a frothy slush unlike anything ever seen in a natural state on earth.

THE PARTICLES AROUND JUPITER
The invisible belt of charged particles that embraces Jupiter is shown here in purple colour. The planet itself has been sectioned to show that Jupiter's temperature rises going towards the centre (*red*), and also that it may have no detectable solid surface inside its atmosphere. The magnetic axis, around which the belt has formed, angles away from the axis of rotation.

166

MAGNETIC AXIS   AXIS OF ROTATION

MAGNETIC AXIS   AXIS OF ROTATION

8
The Solar System and Beyond

Comet Ikeya-Seki circles the sun, passes the earth and heads for home—thousands of millions of miles beyond Pluto—late in 1965.

MODERN ASTRONOMERS believe that the solar system is by no means unique; far beyond its boundaries are thousands of millions of other planetary systems. Almost any star in the sky may, like our own sun, have its *entourage* of planets, some of which are likely to support life, even intelligent life. These systems cannot be observed directly, and the best way to reason about them is to gather every possible shred of information about the solar system, which is at present the only example of a planetary system that can be studied in close detail.

The solar system still harbours many mysteries. Most of the information about it comes from the earth, the moon, Venus, Mars and Jupiter, which are relatively easy to observe. But now the techniques of modern astronomy are penetrating the secrets of the planets towards the extremes of the system—Mercury, Saturn, Uranus, Neptune and Pluto—and beyond them the far-ranging comets and the planets of alien stars.

Within the solar system the smallest and innermost planet, Mercury, is notoriously elusive. It is hardly bigger than the moon (3,030 miles in diameter against 2,160 miles), but it is not very distant from the earth, sometimes coming as near as 48,337,000 miles, and it is fairly bright. What makes it so difficult to study is its closeness to the sun; the angle between them is always less than that between the two hands of a watch at 1 o'clock. During the day the sun's blazing light complicates observation of near-by Mercury, and at night the planet disappears from view almost as quickly as the sun does. Mercury can be seen alone only when it is low above the horizon, just before the sun rises or soon after it sets. Observation at such low angles is seldom satisfactory because of the great distance that the planet's light must travel through the earth's murky and turbulent lower atmosphere.

Labouring under these handicaps, the most skilful observers studied Mercury for decades, trying to make a map of its surface. Their progress was slow and uncertain. But eventually most of them reached something like a consensus. Nearly all agreed that the planet revealed only one hemisphere no matter from what direction it was observed. This must mean, they thought, that only one hemisphere was ever illuminated: the planet therefore must always keep the same side towards the sun, just as the moon keeps the same side towards the earth.

Important consequences flowed from this conclusion. If the same side of Mercury always faced the near-by sun, that side must get extremely hot. The dark side, on the other hand, must be the coldest place in the solar system. Hardly any heat would flow from the planet's interior, and no warming winds would blow from the sunlit side. Mercury was then believed to have no atmosphere. If it ever had one in the past, so went the reasoning, the gases would have escaped or migrated to the perpetually dark hemisphere, where they would have been condensed by the cold and deposited in a solid form as immobile as rock. Early observations of infra-red light supported this picture of Mercury by setting the temperature of the sunlit side at 415° C. The dark side gave no infra-red readings at all and was judged to be close to absolute zero, −268° C.

The dramatic hot-and-cold, sun-facing view of Mercury prevailed for many years and can still be found in fairly recent textbooks. It remained unshaken until astronomers estimated the temperature of Mercury's dark side from its radio waves and found it to be at "room temperature", roughly 21° C. This discovery posed a riddle. If the same side always faced away from the sun, as the visual observers insisted, a large movement of heat would be needed to keep the dark side so warm. A dense atmosphere would do this, of course, but new and careful observations showed that, although Mercury does have some atmosphere, its density cannot be more than about one-thousandth of the earth's. To keep the dark side at room temperature, this thin gas would have to circulate at impossible speeds.

Measuring Mercury's rotation by radar

The riddle was finally solved by radar astronomy. In 1965 the great radio telescope on the Caribbean island of Puerto Rico measured the rotation of Mercury by the Doppler shifts of wave length in radar echoes from it. These measurements showed that the planet does not rotate at the proper speed to keep the same hemisphere always facing the sun. Instead of rotating once in 88 days, as would be required to keep up with its orbital motion, it rotates once in about 59 days. This means that Mercury's night is long but not eternal. Sunrise comes—to all sides of the planet—at intervals of about 170 earth days. The surface material and thin atmosphere do not have time to cool off completely before the fierce sunlight starts heating them again.

Even though Mercury does not suffer from eternal heat and eternal cold, as was long thought, it does not seem a hospitable place for life. If it ever had a life-initiating atmosphere of hydrogen and other reducing gases, the heat of the near-by sun probably drove it away in too short a time for life to appear. The thin present atmosphere is likely to be transient, made of gases that came out of the interior rather recently and are too heavy to escape quickly into space. When unmanned spacecraft are sent to examine Mercury, they will probably report meteorite craters like the moon's, but unless something more remarkable is discovered on it, the planet is likely to remain a small, unattractive and uninhabited world, visited seldom if ever by space-age man.

But if space-age man should travel in the other direction—out from the sun—his journey would be much more rewarding. Beyond Jupiter he would encounter the most beautiful of all the planets, Saturn, whose symmetrical rings give it a matchless grace. There is nothing like these rings anywhere else in the solar system and Saturn has, besides, another unique property—its low density. If the whole planet could be placed in water, it would float. Though Saturn looks as solid as any other planet, its density is about the same as that of maple wood.

This low density is not hard to explain. Like Jupiter, Saturn is made almost entirely of hydrogen and helium, with small amounts of other gases and a sprinkling of heavy elements. Its total mass, however, is only about one-third that of Jupiter's and does not provide enough gravitation to compress the gases so tightly. Saturn's diameter therefore is not much less than Jupiter's (75,000 against 88,800 miles) while its density is about half as great. It probably has a central body of solid hydrogen much smaller than Jupiter's, and because the pressure of its atmosphere is lower it remains gaseous to a greater depth than Jupiter does.

Since Saturn is so far from the sun, the top of its atmosphere is naturally colder than Jupiter's. Measurements of infra-red light show that the temperature above the clouds is −170° C., compared to Jupiter's −120° C. The upper atmosphere contains less ammonia and more methane, probably because the extreme cold has caused more of the ammonia to freeze and form the dense clouds seen at lower levels.

In many other respects, however, Saturn does resemble Jupiter. Saturn rotates in about 10 hours, which is slightly slower than Jupiter. It has light and dark bands parallel to its equator, doubtless caused by wind movements. They are not as numerous or sharply defined as Jupiter's, and since they do not exhibit as many fast-changing details, they are believed to be less turbulent. Saturn has nothing like Jupiter's Great Red Spot, but conspicuous temporary markings are occasionally seen on its surface. In 1933, for instance, an enormous white spot many thousand miles in diameter appeared suddenly on the equator and spread into a white band.

Saturn's decorative rings

Saturn's rings are better understood than its interior or atmosphere. During the early years of telescopic astronomy there was much debate about whether the rings were solid or made of many separate bodies. The question was settled conclusively when the speeds of the inner and outer edges of the rings were measured. If the rings were solid, they would have rotated round Saturn like wheels and their outer edges would have moved faster than their inner edges. The opposite turned out to be true. The inner edge of the innermost ring is the fastest-moving, while the slowest is the outer edge of the outermost ring. Each section of each ring is rotating at exactly the same speed as a satellite would at that distance.

This discovery proved that the rings are made of bodies on independent orbits; it did not tell how big they are or what they are made of. But as Saturn moves on its 29-year orbit around the sun, the rings appear to change their angle slowly. The slanted disc turns to a knife-edge and for a short time disappears entirely. No trace of it can be seen with the largest telescope, indicating that the rings are thin.

The more the rings are studied the less substantial they appear. They have no detectable gravitational effect on anything. The way they reflect sunlight indicates that they are made of very small separate particles that cast shadows on each other. Evidence for this is that the rings brighten suddenly by as much as 30 per cent when the earth is directly between Saturn and the sun. At this time the dark shadow of each particle is directly behind it and is therefore hidden from an observer on the earth, making the ring look brighter. (For the same reason the moon's surface, which is covered with small, shadow-casting irregularities, brightens suddenly at full moon.)

Careful study of sunlight reflected from the rings leads to the conclusion that they are made of particles no bigger than grains of sand but rough on the surface, as if covered with microscopic ice crystals. Some astronomers think that the rings are only a few inches thick and that the particles fill 0.5 per cent or less of the volume of the rings.

The origin of the frail but spectacular rings is not yet settled. Possibly the particles in the rings are the remains of matter that never formed a satellite because it was too close to Saturn's powerful gravitation.

For radio astronomers Saturn is a puzzle. It emits microwaves that betray its outer temperature, but no loud chorus of longer waves like Jupiter's. Its silence may mean that it lacks the radiation belt that is the source of most of Jupiter's radio waves. Perhaps it has no magnetism to collect charged particles from the sun and shape them into a radiation belt, the way Jupiter does. But this chain of reasoning is risky; Saturn may be not mute but muffled. The planet may have a strong magnetic field, but the rings may act as a barrier that keeps the magnetism from forming a radiation belt.

Planets beyond the reach of the eye

With Saturn the classical solar system comes to an end. Besides the sun, earth and moon, only five planets—Mercury, Venus, Mars, Jupiter and Saturn—were known to the ancients. Even after the invention of the telescope, nearly two centuries had to pass before the British astronomer Sir William Herschel, in 1781, accidentally found a small faint disc among the point-like images of the stars. At first he thought it was a comet, but after a few months its orbit proved it to be a planet. Herschel named it Georgium Sidus (George's Star) after King George III, but later it was renamed Uranus after a pagan god, like the other planets.

Uranus did not behave quite as it should. Year after year its orbit deviated from what was considered its proper course, and astronomers began to suspect that another, yet-to-be-found planet was influencing its orbit. In 1842, John C. Adams, a young mathematics student at Cambridge University, attacked the difficult problem of calculating the position of the supposed planet. In September 1845 he timidly asked Sir George Biddle Airy, England's Astronomer Royal, and James Challis, director of the Cambridge Observatory, to take a look at the sky where he thought the unknown planet should be. Neither of the lordly astronomers considered Adams important enough to be taken seriously.

Meanwhile the French astronomer Urbain Jean Joseph Leverrier made the same calculations and came to almost exactly the same conclusions. Leverrier was a famous man and when he communicated his results in 1846 he got quick attention. On the 23rd September the German astronomer Johann Gottfried Galle found the planet where Leverrier

SIX SATURN SATELLITES are depicted on this 1686 medal, one of a series honouring accomplishments during the reign of France's Louis XIV. In this period the Italian astronomer Giovanni Domenico Cassini, first director of the Paris Observatory, discovered four Saturn satellites as well as a major gap in the planet's rings—called the Cassini Division.

told him to look. It was named Neptune after another god. At the time Leverrier got all the honour for its discovery, but modern astronomers now give equal credit to Adams.

Both Uranus and Neptune are very hard to observe because of their great distances from the earth, Uranus being 1,782 million miles from the sun and Neptune 2,784 million miles. Uranus is somewhat larger (diameter about 30,000 miles), while Neptune (diameter about 28,000 miles) is slightly more dense and massive. Both rotate rapidly, Uranus in 10 hours 49 minutes and Neptune in about 15 hours. Both are Jupiter-type planets, made almost entirely of light materials that are gases at ordinary earthly temperatures.

Spectroscopy shows that Uranus has a large amount of methane, but all of its ammonia has presumably been frozen out of the atmosphere by its low cloud temperatures, about $-185°$ C. It shows faint wind bands and therefore is probably covered with ammonia clouds in slow circulation. Neptune, whose cloud temperature is perhaps 10 degrees colder, has methane but no detectable ammonia. No wind bands have been reported on it, but some observers claim to have seen vague and uncertain blotchy markings.

Whether life is possible on the four big outer planets depends on whether they have regions in their atmospheres where water exists as a liquid and where energy is available in some effective form. Jupiter probably has such a region; Saturn may have one. Uranus and Neptune are progressively less promising, but both probably have the chemical elements needed for life. Until more is known about these two distant planets it would be rash to state categorically that neither of them has any zone between its cold atmosphere and presumably hot interior where chemical reactions that result in life can take place.

The great search for Pluto

The final member of the solar system was found in the same remarkable way as Neptune but with much greater difficulty. The American astronomer Percival Lowell, the proponent of the Martian canals, became convinced that even after the influence of Neptune had been accounted for the orbit of Uranus was still misbehaving. Neptune's orbit, which was less well known, showed similar disturbance. Both Lowell and Professor William H. Pickering of Harvard University decided that the disturbing influence was an unknown "Planet X" and started to calculate its probable position. Lowell published his results in 1915, and his private observatory in Arizona searched the sky for the planet. Success did not come as quickly as it had for Leverrier. Not until 14 years after Lowell's death in 1916 did Clyde Tombaugh, an astronomer at Arizona, who used a specially designed telescope, find the elusive planet. It is so small and dim that it can hardly be distinguished from faint stars near it; but its slow motion on its 248-year orbit shows that it is a planet. It was named Pluto after still another pagan god, but the first two letters of its name are Percival Lowells' initials.

A PLANET PROPHET. French astronomer Urbain Jean Joseph Leverrier, commemorated in the medal above, correctly predicted the existence of Neptune in 1846 by calculations based on orbital irregularities of Uranus. But among the nine planets personified on the reverse of the medal (*below*) is Vulcan, which Leverrier positioned between Mercury and the sun. Although tentative evidence of Vulcan's presence is occasionally reported, its existence has yet to be confirmed.

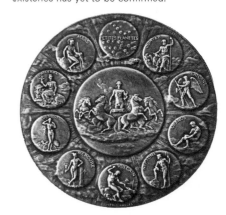

Not much is known about Pluto. Neither its mass nor density can be stated with certainty. Its diameter is about half that of the earth. Its elliptical orbit takes it from 2,790 million to 4,650 million miles from the sun. Small, cold and dark, Pluto is the planet least likely to support life.

The cold outer fringes beyond Pluto are the realm of the comets, those spectacular visitors that make quick dashes around the sun and disappear, seldom to be seen again. Their name comes from the Greek word meaning "long-haired", and refers to the luminous tails, like long hair blowing in the wind, that they develop when they approach the sun. During the ages of superstition they were feared as ill omens, and only recently has a good explanation been found for their behaviour.

A cloud made of comets

Most astronomers now believe that a great thin cloud of comets surrounds the outermost planets, reaching out more than 10 million million miles, almost half way to the nearest stars. In this dark domain, where the sun looks no brighter than many another star, are more than 100,000 million cometary nuclei. Most of them are a mile or so in diameter, though a few may reach diameters exceeding 50 miles. They are not necessarily spherical in shape. They may be irregular, and some astronomers believe they are composed of many small bodies travelling in company. While still resident in the cloud they do not look at all like comets. They are non-luminous and are made mostly of "ices"—that is, ordinary water ice mixed with solidified gases such as methane, carbon dioxide and ammonia. They are porous and their density is very low, probably about 10 per cent of water, or about that of balsa wood. Their surfaces may be covered with feathery structures like newly fallen snow-flakes, but the ices inside are mixed with specks of dust that make them look like dirty packed snow. The general character of these curious objects has been learned by patient observation, but how or where they were formed is not certain. They may be small examples of the same condensation that formed all the planets out of gas and dust.

Most of the thousands of millions of comets stay in their great cloud, moving slowly on enormous orbits around the far-distant sun, but at long intervals some of them are disturbed by the gravitation of a passing star. A few of these move into interstellar space and are lost to the solar system. Others veer towards the sun, eventually to become the brilliant, long-tailed comets that are seen from the earth.

At first the comets move very slowly; the sun is so far away that they hardly feel its pull. But every hour, day and year they move a little faster, and the sun ahead grows brighter. After a comet has come close enough to cross the orbits of the outermost planets, its surface is warmed by the strengthening sunlight, and some of its more volatile

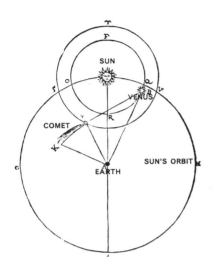

A COMET'S ORBIT was established by Danish astronomer Tycho Brahe with this diagram of the solar system published in 1577. In it he included four members of the system: the sun, the earth, Venus and a comet. Although he clung to the idea that the sun revolved round the earth, he broke with tradition by having Venus and the comet orbit the sun. The orbit he computed for the comet was incorrect, but he proved that comets were bona fide members of the solar system, shattering the prevalent notion that they were luminous atmospheric disturbances.

A.D. 70

174

material begins to turn to gas. A few of its icy "feathers" break off and follow the nucleus on its orbit in a rapidly growing cloud.

By the time a good-sized comet has crossed the orbit of Jupiter, the cloud surrounding its nucleus—called a head, or coma—is big enough to be seen with a telescope. As it plunges still nearer the sun, more gas evaporates, taking some of the dust along into space. The head swells enormously, sometimes exceeding 100,000 miles in diameter, and a brilliant tail begins to extend in the direction away from the sun. It is made of dust and gas driven out of the head by the pressure of sunlight and the "wind" of charged particles shot out of the sun. Sometimes the tail of a large comet is 50 million miles long, and the whole comet shines more brightly than anything in the sky except the sun and moon.

Around the sun at a million miles an hour

The evaporating gases leave behind a good part of the comet's dust as a layer that partially protects the underlying ices from the sun's heat, and this insulation helps them to survive their encounters with the sun. If they pass very close, they whip around it with enormous speed, more than one million miles per hour, and shoot off into space with their tails pointing ahead, carried away from the sun by its light and particles.

Most comets depart on long, elliptical orbits that take them millions of millions of miles into space and keep them safe in outer darkness for thousands of years, but a few do not escape from the sun so easily. If they happen to pass near a large planet, particularly Jupiter, its gravitation may shunt them into short-period orbits around the sun. They then return repeatedly, each time losing a portion of their substance. When all their ices are gone, they disintegrate, leaving a stream of small particles that gradually spreads out thinly and loses its identity.

Every year the earth passes through several of these skeleton comets whose specks of dust shine briefly as shooting stars in the night sky. These cometary meteors, which are sometimes fairly bright, never hit the earth's surface, probably because they are made of fragile material that disintegrates quickly in the atmosphere. (The very bright fireballs that survive their passage through the atmosphere and hit the surface of the earth or come near it have nothing to do with comets, but are wandering chunks of metal or rocky material from the asteroid belt.)

The great cloud of the comets is the most distant province of the solar system. Beyond it lie the stars, at least 100,000 million of them in the sun's own galaxy, the Milky Way. The question of whether they have planets has long been asked. The answer, which is now being given with increasing confidence, is yes. Astronomers now believe that all the stars were formed in the same way, by condensing out of gas, or gas and dust, and that planets are normal by-products of this process. Since the sun is an

THREE BRILLIANT COMETS terrified early observers, who considered them to be omens of disaster and described them as shown in these 17th-century illustrations : a sword, a sabre and a feather. Despite Tycho Brahe's 1577 definition of comets as bodies which orbited the sun like planets (*opposite*), the notion long persisted that comets presaged war or pestilence—disasters which occurred regularly enough to lend substance to the belief.

1049   1618

ordinary star, there is nothing special about it and its planetary system. Other stars can have planets too, and positive evidence is accumulating that many of them do.

Why some stars wobble

No telescope can directly detect a planet revolving around a star; even the nearest stars are too far away. But planets can be detected by indirect methods. The most successful technique so far requires many accurate pictures which can be compared to reveal the star's motion. All near-by stars show "proper motion"—that is, motion of their own, not apparent motion that is due to any effect of the earth's movements on observations. If a star's proper motion wobbles slightly, the star must have with it at least one companion that cannot be seen. The wobble appears because the star and its unseen companion are actually revolving around a common centre, like partners in a waltz, but only the large star can be seen. If the mass of the large star is known, as is sometimes the case, the mass and orbit of the companion can be calculated.

This method of detecting the companions of stars by the wobble they cause can be used only on stars that are the sun's closest neighbours, and it has not detected objects smaller than Jupiter. Its success, nevertheless, has been extraordinary. Barnard's star, the nearest single star to the sun, turns out to have an invisible, or dark companion with only 1.5 times the mass of Jupiter. This is the smallest planet discovered beyond the solar system so far, but 3 out of the 12 stars nearest to the sun are already known to have some sort of dark companion. It is safe to assume that if a star has one planet it very likely has others formed by the same process, and that stars too distant to be examined for planets are likely to have them too. In fact, it appears that planetary systems are common possessions of stars. It is probable that the Milky Way galaxy with its 100,000 million stars has several hundred thousand million planets, and there may be comparable numbers in other galaxies.

How many of these innumerable planets may have life? The answer to this fascinating question depends on a large number of unknown factors. Planets that are similar to the earth in mass, surface temperature, atmosphere and history are probably relatively rare, but this strict set of conditions may not be necessary. If it turns out that life can exist on planets like Mars or Jupiter, the number of favourable habitats will be enormously increased. It is also possible that life can appear on planets that do not resemble any examples in the solar system. But even if strict conditions are necessary, the statistics are strongly in favour of life.

A great deal of thought, some of it intelligent, has been invested in speculation about the creatures that may inhabit planets or other environments throughout the universe. One school of thought believes that life requires conditions narrowly similar to those on earth and will develop—if it develops at all—along similar lines. Advocates of this doctrine of convergence point out that cold-blooded, water-breathing tuna and warm-blooded, air-breathing porpoises are only distantly related, but they have closely similar forms because they both need excellent streamlining to move through the water rapidly. Therefore, in this view, large land animals that evolve on an alien planet somewhat like the earth are apt to have four limbs and a head containing their mouth and principal sense organs, because this is the most effective pattern.

The whole convergence idea is challenged by the broader view that life can develop under widely different conditions and take widely different forms. It is possible to imagine any number of novel environments and design living organisms to fit them, but no one should flatter himself that he can do it correctly. According to this doctrine of divergence, the outcome of evolution is largely a matter of chance, even though living conditions in various places may be closely similar.

The earth's modern organisms have some 4,000 million years of history behind them, during which evolution explored innumerable blind alleys. Every large, advanced creature is the product of literally thousands of millions of mutations, most of them imperceptible, which had the effect of giving the creature's ancestors, age after age, a survival advantage over their competitors. Under slightly different conditions, or as the result of mere accidents, a different form might have won the battle for continuance. Many evolutionists believe that if the primitive earth were to evolve life all over again, there would be no appreciable chance that an animal physically resembling man, or even any of the mammals, would evolve.

Intelligent life on other planets

The question of whether alien planets have intelligent beings on them is a still-more tangled one. It is by no means certain that intelligence of human quality is the normal culmination of evolution. Some conditions may be favourable to life but not to high intelligence. The earth's oceans, for instance, have no appreciably intelligent creatures, except for mammals such as porpoises and seals that have returned to the water. To judge by this analogy, which is risky, an alien planet that is completely covered by water will probably have no animals more intelligent than the earth's fish. The human combination of large brain and tool-holding hand is even more fortuitous. A long series of special circumstances was necessary to develop it. If any of them had been lacking, the earth might have continued for thousands of millions of years more, perhaps for the life of the solar system, without achieving really high intelligence.

On the other hand, intelligence undoubtedly has important survival value. Evolution on the earth has generally moved in the direction of more highly developed brains. Fish have better brains than the marine worms from which they evolved, and amphibians, reptiles and mammals have successively better ones. If man had not developed his large brain, some other mammal, perhaps the raccoon, might have done so in a few tens of millions of years. Evolutionists point out that man's ancestor 70 million years ago is believed to have been something like the tiny, fierce tree shrew. Raccoons seem much more promising. According to this school of thought, intelligence is in the cards for any planet where conditions are reasonably favourable for it.

But does intelligence imply that civilization exists? Here is another question hedged with unknowns. In the case of the earth, more than 200,000 years passed between the appearance of the first men with really large brains and the first human societies that can be called civilized. But with only one example to judge by, this incubation period cannot be called standard for all inhabited planets. It may be unusually short or long. In many cases, there should be plenty of time. The earth produced creatures capable of technical civilization in about 5,000 million years, less than half of the 13,000 million years that the sun is expected to shine steadily. Since smaller stars of the sun's type are extremely numerous and shine even longer, their planetary systems will have an even better chance—so far as time is concerned—to develop civilizations.

Even when civilization has begun, a high technical civilization is by no means certain. The first civilized human communities were agricultural villages in the Middle East about 10,000 years ago. Since that time human civilization has experienced many ups and downs. There was a major decline after the early flourishing of the ancient empires in Egypt and Mesopotamia and a parallel dark age after the fall of the Roman Empire. Other cultural centres, such as China, also had dark ages. For many long periods it must have seemed that civilization was a self-limiting process that could never rise above the handicraft level.

Civilizations in outer space

At present human culture is in an unprecedented state of rapid development. For the first time it has become technical and scientific and has found ways to unlock an apparently limitless storehouse of new powers. Its progress grows faster and faster; all its curves soar upwards, and the limit is nowhere in sight. It is tempting to assume that civilizations on other planets normally reach the same take-off point and become as progressive and powerful as the earth's. Another step is to expect that if they are a thousand or a million years older, they must be vastly more advanced than the earth's civilization.

Neither of these assumptions can be justified by studying the single example of advanced civilization that we possess—that is, our own. Alien civilizations may not develop in the same way as the earth's. They may exhaust totally the ready resources of their planet and return to a more primitive condition. Their individuals and societies may be repelled by change and make sure that it does not take place. They may destroy themselves with all-too-effective weapons.

It can be argued, however, that high civilization has survival value and will therefore be favoured by cultural evolution. A civilized group will generally prove stronger than a primitive one, and a high technical civilization will overcome a culture that clings to pre-technical ways. This has happened so often on the earth that it seems to be a law of nature. It is happening now and therefore, say the optimists, it is safe to assume that some of the planets that have developed intelligent life far in the past will have achieved technical civilization and soared far beyond the earth in knowledge and power.

If wonderful civilizations exist among the stars, it is only natural that human beings would want to visit them, or at least to communicate with them. Both these enterprises are fantastically difficult. Even the nearest stars are so enormously far away that to reach them not only must space be overcome, but also time. If a space ship sets out for near-by Barnard's star, about six light-years away, at the steady speed of 100,000 miles per hour, the voyage will take 40,000 years, and before it is fairly begun the crew will die of old age. Travel at greater speed, even at a major fraction of the speed of light, will not help much, especially for journeys to more distant and more interesting stars.

A 200-year trip in 20 years

Besides the unattractive recourse of putting the crew in deep freeze for thousands of years, the only known way out of this impasse is to travel close to the speed of light itself, the ultimate speed limit of the universe. If this can be accomplished, an extraordinary thing will happen. As one of the strange consequences of relativity, time will slow down in the space ship, and the men will reach their destination in what for them will be a few years. Suppose, for instance, that a space ship sets out for a star 100 light-years away and accelerates steadily at the rate of a falling object on the earth. After the ship passes the mid-point of its journey, it decelerates at the same rate. During most of the trip it will be moving at close to the speed of light. For members of the crew, time will slow down, but they will feel no difference, and the round trip will take only 20 of their years. For the people they left behind on earth, time will not slow down. More than 200 years will have passed before the ship returns, and the great-grandchildren of the crew will be dead.

Even the most hopeful would-be travellers of interstellar space do not believe that such a relativistic journey will be possible in the immediate future. But they are confident that one day the trip will be made. They rely on the ever-increasing speed of human technical and scientific progress. Three hundred years ago no one on earth had even seen the crudest working steam-engine. Now the earth has spacecraft that journey to Mars. Three hundred years hence the men of the future may well have discovered some unsuspected way to travel to the stars.

Until that time approaches, the most promising way to make contact with high civilizations on alien planetary systems is to listen for radio messages from them. Though difficult, this is by no means impossible. Radio telescopes no larger than those existing today on the earth could communicate with similar telescopes on planets tens of light-years away. Within that distance are thousands of stars, many of which are sure to have planets, and it is quite possible that radio messages from civilizations on some of them are reaching the earth now. The first sign that life exists among the stars may be radio signals that mark meaningful pulses on the recording tape of an earthly radio telescope.

OTHER SOLAR SYSTEMS that have been detected in our galaxy are listed below. Each consists of a near-by star and at least one planet which orbits it as the earth orbits the sun. None of these planets has ever been seen. But astronomers have deduced their presence and size by studying the motions of the stars closest to earth. Those moving in wavering paths are believed to be affected by the gravitational attraction of planets. Although the planets may be up to 20 times the mass of Jupiter, they are too small and reflect too little light to be seen from earth. The shaded area contains the names of stars whose companions, while strongly suspected, have not yet been confirmed. There may be many more bodies in each system, but only the largest can be detected with the present technique.

STAR	DISTANCE FROM EARTH (LIGHT-YEARS)	MASS OF COMPANION RELATIVE TO JUPITER
BARNARD'S STAR	6.1	1.5
LALANDE 21185	7.9	10
61 CYGNI	11.1	8
BD + 5° 1668	12.4	20
CI 2354	15.1	20
BD + 20° 2465	15.5	20
BD + 43° 4305	15.7	20
CIN 2347	25.5	20

Life on
Other Worlds

Man has always been fascinated by the possibility of life on other worlds. As long ago as the second century, science fiction writers were peopling the universe with bizarre creatures. When scientists began to develop instruments capable of analysing distant planets, they generally dismissed the possibility of extraterrestrial life. The atmospheres and temperature ranges of those planets seemed too different from those of earth, which is still the only known life-supporting planet. In recent years, however, scientists have begun to change their minds. They understand how life might have originated under conditions that would appear alien to us now. At the dawn of life on earth, its atmosphere probably resembled that of such apparently hostile planets as Jupiter. Accepting the possibility of life is one thing. Proving it is another. Great interplanetary distance, suggested by the scale drawing on the right, is still the major obstacle to exploration. But scientists are developing the machines and techniques for finding life, preparing for the inevitable day when those distances are spanned—and man makes his first contact with living beings on another world.

PLANETS ON AN EARTHLY SCALE
Interplanetary distance, the greatest obstacle to the discovery of life, is suggested in the map on the right, drawn to a scale of 150 miles to 93 million miles—the distance from the sun to the earth. If the solar system were shrunk and placed on a map of Europe and Africa, the sun would be in Norway while Pluto, the farthest planet, would lie 6,500 miles south at the Cape of Good Hope.

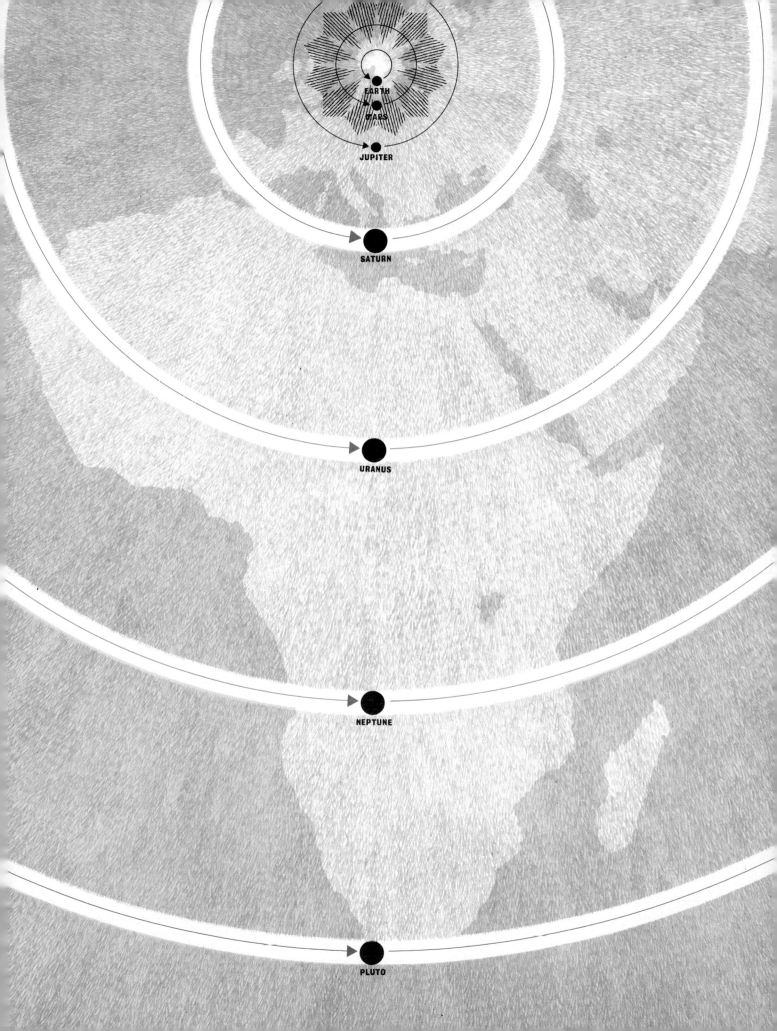

EARTH

MARS

JUPITER

SATURN

URANUS

NEPTUNE

PLUTO

Far from the Warming Sun

Incapable of supporting any form of life: that was once the undisputed verdict on the four outermost planets—Saturn (*above*), Neptune, Uranus and Pluto (*opposite*). The evidence was their extremely low temperatures and their complete lack of oxygen.

But this verdict is now open to reasonable doubt. The fact that Saturn, Uranus and Neptune have atmospheres at all suggests the presence of life's precursors. Though Pluto probably has little or no atmosphere—and so is much less likely to sustain life

—recent discoveries have shown that the atmospheres of the other three are chemically suitable for reactions that may be sufficient to begin life.

Also these distant planets are definitely not, as was once believed, uniformly subject to temperatures of −170°C. and below. The wan heat of the sun combined with the internal warmth emitted by the planets has been permanently trapped beneath their atmospheric envelopes. Temperatures on some of these planets are now believed to be comparable to that of a heated room on earth.

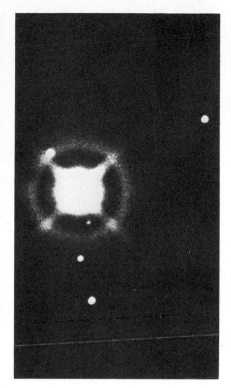

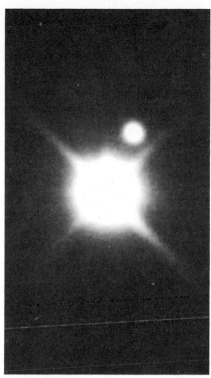

ONE OF A PAIR
Given a star-like sparkle by distortion in the telescopic lens, Uranus (*above*) hovers in the midst of its five satellites. Uranus's heavy atmosphere traps enough heat to foster the development of life. Even more exciting are indications of molecules which have yet to be identified.

A BRIGHT RESEMBLANCE
Neptune, a near-twin of Uranus, is shown with Triton, the closer, and larger, of its two satellites. Half again as far from the sun as Uranus, it may indeed harbour life, for spectroscopic studies show that its atmosphere has sufficient hydrogen to produce organic molecules.

THE RINGED BEHEMOTH
Like a baleful eye, Saturn spins inside its rings of ice crystals (*above*). Although they have a diameter of 171,000 miles, more than twice that of Saturn itself, the rings are only a few inches thick. Saturn also has ten satellites, not seen in this close-up photograph. Titan, the largest of them, has an atmosphere, but like Pluto it seems to be too cold to sustain life.

THE OUTERMOST WANDERER
Pluto is so far away that it was not identified as a planet until 1930. It is so cold that, even if it has an atmosphere, the likelihood of life is extremely small. Even through powerful telescopes it looks like a dim star, but these photographs offer proof that it is indeed a planet: taken a day apart, they show the movement of Pluto among apparently motionless stars.

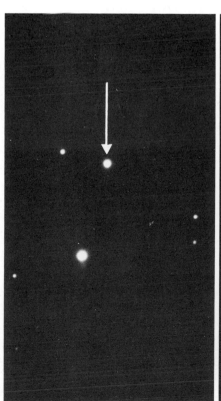

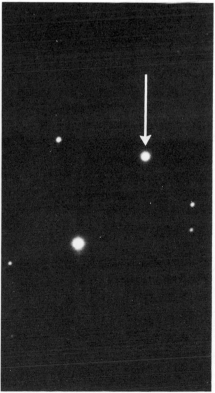

A Universe Teeming with Life

Despite its 10,000-million-mile diameter, the solar system, presided over by the sun (*below*), is dwarfed by the Milky Way galaxy to which it belongs. But the Milky Way itself, containing 100,000 million stars, is only a mote in the universe. There are thousands of millions of such galaxies, each with its own myriad stars, and most of these stars have their own planetary systems. If only 1/10,000 of 1 per cent of those planets harbours a technical civilization—a conservative estimate —the universe must teem with more than 100 million million civilizations,

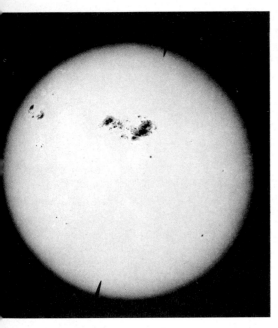

OUR STAR, THE SUN
Despite its importance to life on earth, the sun, 864,000 miles in diameter (shown here darkly spotted with huge regions of cooler gases), is only an average star in size, brilliance and age. It lies three-quarters of the distance from the centre to the edge of one of the galaxy's spiral arms.

A BRIGHT COMMUNITY OF SUNS
The Milky Way galaxy (*right*) is a flat, spiralling mass of stars. This view is towards the centre, 30,000 light-years from earth; the entire galaxy is 80,000 light-years wide. The sun, revolving around the centre at 480,000 m.p.h., takes 250 million years to complete a single circuit.

M31, THE MILKY WAY'S TWIN

The great galaxy M31 in the constellation Andromeda, 2.2 million light-years away, is similar to the Milky Way in appearance, with its spiral arms swirling out of the bright, densely packed nucleus. The two glowing discs above and below M31 are smaller satellite galaxies.

GALAXIES LIKE GRAINS OF SAND

A cluster of galaxies glitter at the outer range of the 200-inch telescope at Mount Palomar, California. They are seen as they existed a thousand million years ago; they are so far away that their light, even at its speed of 186,000 miles per second, took that long to travel to the earth.

The Origin of Life

In the aeons before life began, the atmosphere of earth was mainly methane, ammonia, hydrogen and water—a mixture that would kill most modern earthly life. But paradoxically—as scientists now know—these very gases were necessary for the beginnings of life. Prodded to react with each other by some form of energy—lightning or ultra-violet light—they formed the chemical compounds from which all life on earth has evolved.

To demonstrate this, scientists performed an experiment with the apparatus on the right. Through a mixture of gases like those in earth's primordial atmosphere, they shot bolts of simulated lightning. The energy released caused a chemical reaction which yielded amino-acids and other compounds found in all known life.

Since there are other planets, such as Jupiter, whose atmospheres are very much like the young earth's, researchers tried another experiment. In the device on the far right, they subjected the experimental atmosphere of methane and ammonia to the low temperatures of Jupiter. Even under such conditions, a spark produced organic compounds.

The results of both tests have encouraged space scientists to develop the portable laboratory below. Refined and adapted to an unmanned space craft, working models of such a laboratory will be sent out to distant planets. There they will search for the organic molecules that may be the beginning of the evolution of life.

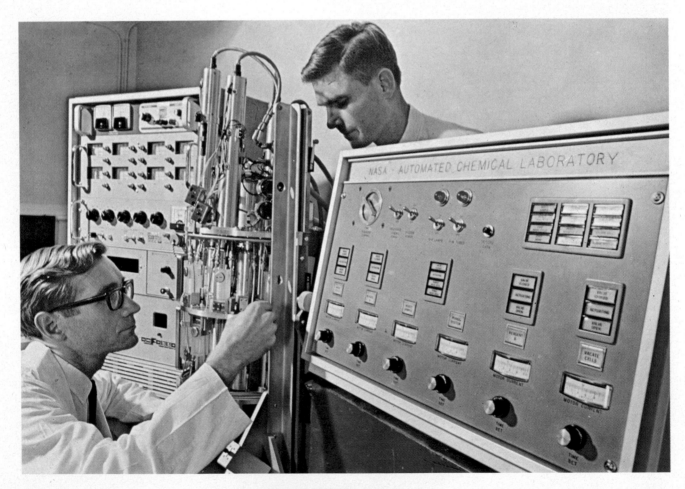

AN EXTRATERRESTRIAL LAB
A miniaturized version of this automated chemical laboratory may one day radio back to earth the first reports of life-suggesting molecules. Carried to some distant planet by an unmanned space vehicle, the device will gather samples of soil by means of a scoop or suction mechanism. Then its test-tube assembly (*centre*) will analyse the samples by means of ultra-violet light and light-sensitive photoelectric cells. The console panel (*right*) supplies the prototype with computerized guidance; the panel (*left*) provides the electric power for the laboratory.

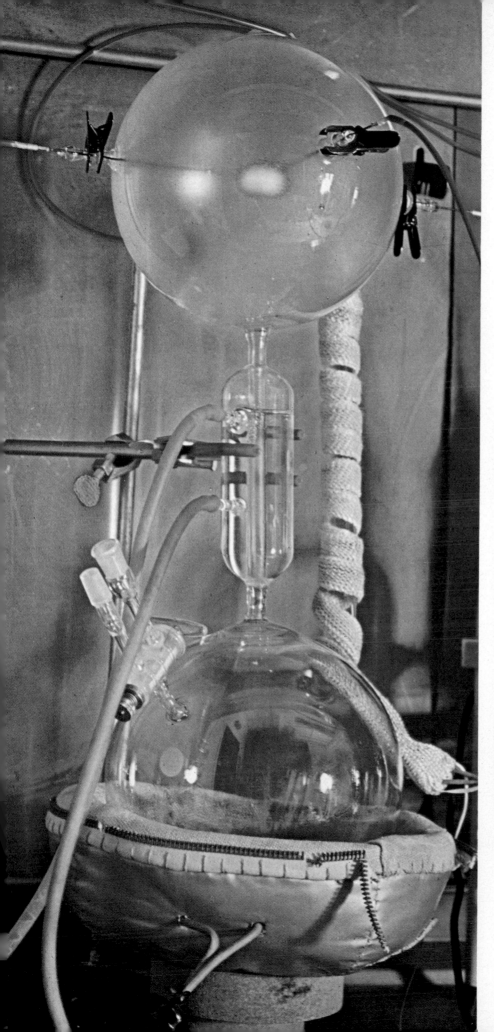

A SPARK THAT MAY LEAD TO LIFE

A high-voltage electric spark arcs through a globe (*left*) containing a mixture of gases similar to those that comprised the earth's atmosphere more than 4,000 million years ago. The resulting chemical reaction causes the formation of amino acids and other building blocks common to all life on the earth. Heavier than the gases, these compounds travel through the connecting tubes and are collected in the lower globe.

AN IMITATION OF JUPITER

Wreathed in streamers of evaporating liquid nitrogen, a Jupiter simulator at Ames Research Laboratories in Mountain View, California, contains a mixture of methane and ammonia. Cooled by the nitrogen to −180°C., this atmosphere is roughly similar to Jupiter's. A spark creates various carbon compounds that are an early step in the development of life.

The Importance of Adaptation

It seems impossible that any form of life could survive continued exposure to the intense radiation produced by a nuclear reactor (*opposite*). Yet, one form of bacteria was found thriving within inches of the reactor's heart— its glowing atomic pile.

This is only one extreme example of the adaptability of life on earth. Penguins and lichens withstand the hostility of the Poles; lizards and cactus plants survive in the desert despite an almost total lack of water; fish live miles below the ocean's surface under pressures that would crush the toughest machine.

To exobiologists, who study the possibility of life on other worlds, the radiation-resistant bacteria were especially exciting, for they added yet another "intolerable" condition to the growing list of hostile environments in which, it is now known, life can survive. These scientists have already studied the effects on life of the hard conditions of other worlds. They have shown that earth-grown moulds (*left*) and even some cactus plants can live in a Mars-like atmosphere at low temperatures and virtually deprived of oxygen and water.

MICRO-ORGANISMS AND MARS
Despite the fact that they have been deprived of water and oxygen for several months, a group of moulds gathered at random from soil and plants (shown in the illustration above) lead healthy lives. Their home for several months was a Mars simulator, a small enclosure in which the atmosphere, temperature and length of day have been made similar to the actual conditions to be found on the planet Mars.

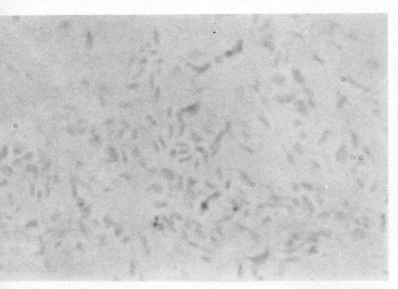

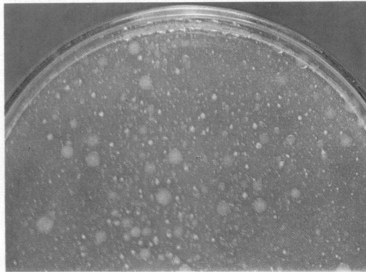

UNHARMED BY DEADLY RAYS
In the pink of health, pseudomonas bacteria (*above, left*) collected from the core of an atomic reactor survived radiation 1,000 times as strong as scientists had considered lethal to most bacteria. After being removed, the adaptable bacteria retained the ability to grow and multiply in a normal culture medium (*above, right*). At one bacteria-infested reactor (*opposite*), life-belts facetiously initialled SS ORR (Oak Ridge Reactor) are actually of vital importance—unlike the bacteria, a man in the water could be hurt or killed by the intense radiation.

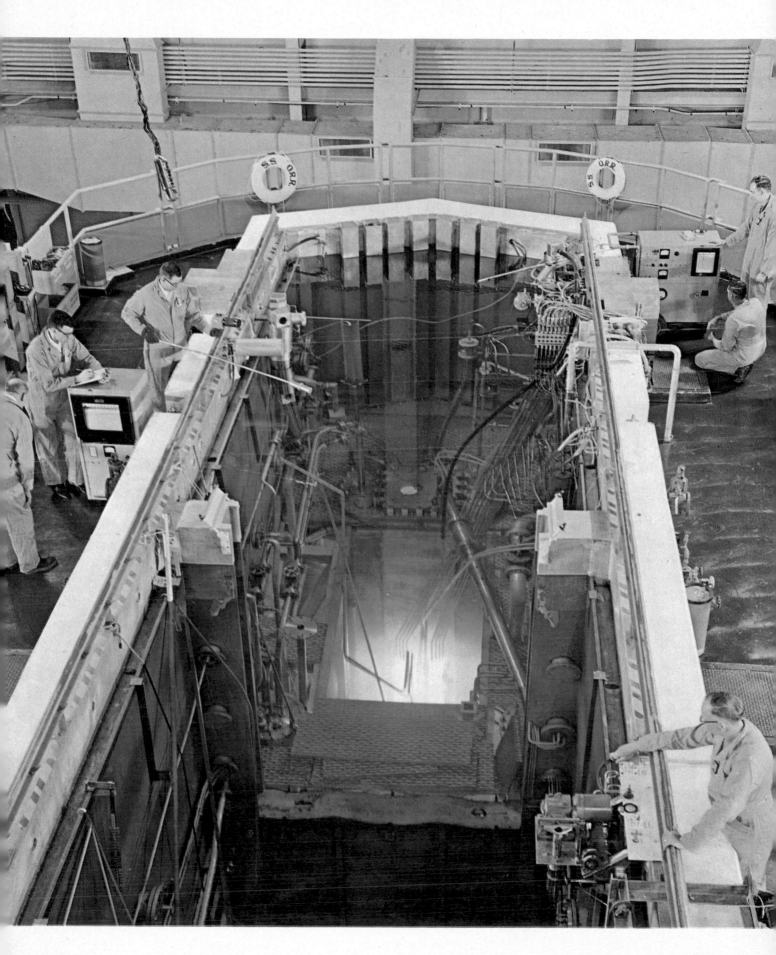

The Weird Forms
Life May Take

Like jet engines with eyes, the imaginary creatures on these pages propel themselves by inhaling the atmosphere through their gaping mouths, expelling it in rearward spurts. The hydrogen it provides gives them shape and buoyancy. Like whales eating plankton, they take in organic material formed in the atmosphere and use the material as food.

These strange beings are one example of the alien forms scientists think extraterrestrial life may take. Literally gas-bags, they could be the inhabitants of a Jupiter-like planet circling some distant star system.

These creatures would probably be no more typical of life throughout the universe than man is. Like dolphins, they could be intelligent. But lack of limbs, a necessity for building, would make them unsuited for a technical civilization. Their shape is especially adapted to their environment, a planet whose atmosphere is hydrogen, water, methane and ammonia. Such a planet—a ball of gaseous material that became progressively more dense from cloud tops to centre—would offer its creatures no solid surfaces. They would live suspended like blimps in a cloudy world.

LIFE UNDER A DOUBLE SUN
On their planet, gas-bags hover in the light of two stars, one (blue) hotter than its companion. Surrounded by an envelope of gases, such double stars are common, but not all boast a Jupiter-like planet. Such a world must orbit far from its double sun. It might otherwise circle only one of the pair or travel in a figure 8 between them, causing extreme changes in temperature.

The Solar System's Planets and Satellites

Like pieces of a puzzle, all the bits of data the astronomer gathers about the planets and their travelling companions the satellites serve to clarify his total view of the solar system. For example, by computing the mass of a planet and its diameter, he can estimate its gravity in terms of a man's weight and even draw some meaningful conclusions about the composition of its atmosphere. Armed with data about the planet's motion and atmosphere, he can then speculate intelligently on the possibility of life there. Similar deductions also reveal fascinating information about the 32 known satellites, which, while prisoners of the planets, often display quite different compositions and characteristics.

THE PLANETS

PLANET	AVERAGE DISTANCE FROM SUN (MILES)	ROTATION PERIOD (EARTH UNITS)	LENGTH OF YEAR (EARTH UNITS)	DIAMETER (MILES)	MASS RELATIVE TO EARTH	EQUIVALENT WEIGHT OF 150-LB. PERSON	COMPOSITION OF ATMOSPHERE
Mercury	36,000,000	59 days (approx.)	88.0 days	3,000	0.05	55	carbon dioxide
Venus	67,000,000	249 days (approx.)	224.7 days	7,600	0.81	130	nitrogen? carbon dioxide, water
Earth	93,000,000	23.9 hours	365.3 days	7,900	1.00	150	nitrogen, oxygen, water, carbon dioxide, argon
Mars	142,000,000	24.6 hours	687.0 days	4,200	0.11	55	carbon dioxide, nitrogen? water
Jupiter	486,000,000	9.8 hours	11.9 years	89,000	317.8	380	hydrogen, helium, methane, ammonia, water? neon?
Saturn	892,000,000	10.2 hours	29.5 years	75,000	95.2	160	same as Jupiter
Uranus	1,800,000,000	10.8 hours	84.0 years	30,000	14.5	155	hydrogen, helium, methane, ammonia? water? neon?
Neptune	2,800,000,000	15 hours	164.8 years	28,000	17.2	210	same as Uranus
Pluto	3,700,000,000	6.4 days	248.4 years	3,600	0.11 (approx.) unknown		unknown

THE SATELLITES

PLANET	KNOWN SATELLITES (IN ORDER OF DISTANCE FROM PLANET)	YEAR AND PLACE OF DISCOVERY	DISCOVERER	AVERAGE DISTANCE FROM PLANET (MILES)	ORBITAL TIME (EARTH DAYS)	DIAMETER (MILES)
Mercury	none					
Venus	none					
Earth	Moon			240,000	27.3	2,200
Mars	Phobos	1877, U.S.	A. Hall	5,800	0.3	5 (approx.)
	Deimos	1877, U.S.	A. Hall	15,000	1.3	3 (approx.)
Jupiter	V	1892, U.S.	E. Barnard	110,000	0.5	70 (approx.)
	I (Io)	1610, Italy	Galileo	260,000	1.8	2,000
	II (Europa)	1610, Italy	Galileo	420,000	3.6	1,800
	III (Ganymede)	1610, Italy	Galileo	670,000	7.2	3,100
	IV (Callisto)	1610, Italy	Galileo	1,200,000	16.7	2,800
	VI	1904, U.S.	C. Perrine	7,100,000	251	50 (approx.)
	VII	1905, U.S.	C. Perrine	7,300,000	260	20 (approx.)
	X	1938, U.S.	S. Nicholson	7,400,000	264	10 (approx.)
	XII	1951, U.S.	S. Nicholson	13,000,000	631	10 (approx.)
	XI	1938, U.S.	S. Nicholson	14,000,000	692	10 (approx.)
	VIII	1908, U.K.	P. Melotte	14,600,000	739	10 (approx.)
	IX	1914, U.S.	S. Nicholson	14,700,000	758	10 (approx.)
Saturn	Janus	1966, France	A. Dollfus	98,000	0.8	190 (approx.)
	Mimas	1789, U.K.	W. Herschel	120,000	0.9	300 (approx.)
	Enceladus	1789, U.K.	W. Herschel	150,000	1.4	400 (approx.)
	Tethys	1684, France	D. Cassini	180,000	1.9	630
	Dione	1684, France	D. Cassini	240,000	2.7	550 (approx.)
	Rhea	1672, France	D. Cassini	330,000	4.5	950
	Titan	1655, The Netherlands	C. Huygens	760,000	15.9	3,000
	Hyperion	1848, U.S.	W. Bond	920,000	21.3	100 (approx.)
	Iapetus	1671, France	D. Cassini	2,200,000	79.3	500 (approx.)
	Phoebe	1898, U.S.	W. Pickering	8,100,000	550	100 (approx.)
Uranus	Miranda	1948, U.S.	G. Kuiper	77,000	1.4	200 (approx.)
	Ariel	1851, U.K.	W. Lassell	120,000	2.5	500 (approx.)
	Umbriel	1851, U.K.	W. Lassell	170,000	4.2	350 (approx.)
	Titania	1787, U.K.	W. Herschel	270,000	8.7	600 (approx.)
	Oberon	1787, U.K.	W. Herschel	360,000	13.5	500 (approx.)
Neptune	Triton	1846, U.K.	W. Lassell	220,000	5.9	2,300
	Nereid	1949, U.S.	G. Kuiper	3,500,000	359	200 (approx.)
Pluto	none					

A Traffic Pattern
for Planets

EARLY IN THE 17TH CENTURY, the great German astronomer Johannes Kepler published his three laws of planetary motion, describing the journey of the planets around the sun with amazing accuracy. Some of his conclusions, based on data left him by Tycho Brahe, were that planets travel in elliptical orbits, that they speed up when close to the sun, and that the inner planets orbit faster than those more distant. Mercury, for instance, travels at around 110,000 m.p.h., while Pluto moves a tenth as fast. Kepler's laws apply to all planets in the solar system, although he knew of only six in his lifetime.

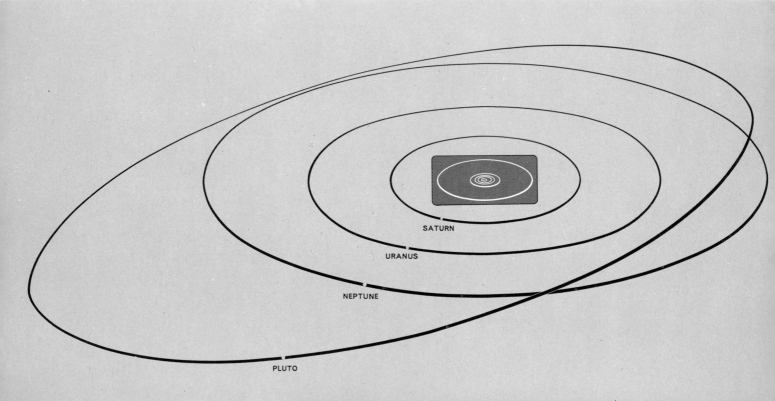

SATURN

URANUS

NEPTUNE

PLUTO

ORDERLY ORBITS
The planetary orbits within the solar system, all governed by Kepler's laws, are shown above and at the right. Modern astronomers, using these laws and complementary physical laws formulated by Newton and Einstein, can now explain all planetary motion, even the eccentric orbit of Pluto. This planet crosses the orbit of neighbouring Neptune, and some scientists believe that Pluto was once a satellite of Neptune.

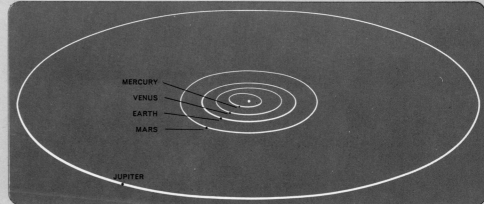

MERCURY
VENUS
EARTH
MARS

JUPITER

FURTHER READING

General

Abell, G. O., *Exploration of the Universe*. Holt, Rinehart and Winston, 1964.

Boeke, Kees, *Cosmic View: The Universe in 40 Jumps*. Faber, 1957.

Clarke, Arthur C., *The Challenge of the Spaceship*. Harper & Row. 1959.

Hoyle, Fred, *Astronomy*. Macdonald & Co., 1962.

*Oparin, A., and V. Fesenkov, *Life in the Universe*. Twayne, New York, 1961.

Struve, Otto, Beverly Lynds and Helen Pillans, *Elementary Astronomy*. Oxford University Press, 1959.

*Struve, Otto, *The Universe*. M.I.T. Press, 1962.

*Weisskopf, Victor F., *Knowledge and Wonder*. Heinemann Educ., 1964.

History of Astronomy

Abetti, Giorgio, *The History of Astronomy*. Sidgwick & Jackson, 1954.

*Dreyer, J. L. E., *A History of Astronomy from Thales to Kepler*. Dover : Constable, 1958.

*Galilei, Galileo, *Discoveries and Opinions of Galileo*. Stillman Drake, ed. Peter Smith, Gloucester, Mass., 1959.

*Geymonat, Ludovico, *Galileo Galilei*. McGraw-Hill, 1965.

Guthrie, W. K. C., *A History of Greek Philosophy*, Vol. I. Cambridge University Press, 1962.

†Kramer, Samuel N., *History Begins at Sumer*. Thames & Hudson, 1958.

Ley, Willy, *Watchers of the Skies*. Sidgwick & Jackson,1964.

*Neugebauer, Otto, *The Exact Sciences in Antiquity*. Harper & Row, 1957.

Pannekoek, A., *A History of Astronomy*. Allen & Unwin, 1961.

Extraterrestrial Life

Dole, Stephen, and Isaac Asimov, *Planets for Man*. Random House, New York, 1964.

Hoyle, Fred, *Of Men and Galaxies*. University of Washington Press, 1964.

Quimby, Freeman, ed., *Concepts for Detection of Extraterrestrial Life*. NASA document SP-56. U.S. Government Printing Office, 1964.

Shklovsky, I. S., and Carl Sagan, *Intelligent Life in the Universe*. Holden-Day, New York, 1966.

Space Science Board, "Biology and the Exploration of Mars." National Academy of Sciences-National Research Council, 1966.

Sullivan, Walter, *We Are Not Alone*. McGraw-Gill, 1964.

Biological Evolution

*Eiseley, L. C., *The Immense Journey*. Gollancz, 1958.

Fox, Sidney W., ed., *The Origins of Prebiological Systems*. Academic Press, 1965.

*Hanson, Earl D., *Animal Diversity* (2nd edition). Prentice-Hall, 1964.

†Rush, J. H., *The Dawn of Life*. English University Press, 1962.

*Simpson, George Gaylord, *The Meaning of Evolution*. Yale University Press, 1949.

†Young, Richard S., and Cyril Ponnamperuma, *Early Evolution of Life*. American Institute of Biological Sciences, BSCS Pamphlets No. 11, 1964.

Tools and Techniques

King, Henry C., *History of the Telescope*. Griffin, 1955.

Miczaika, G. R., and William M. Sinton, *Tools of the Astronomer*. Harvard : Oxford University Press, 1961.

†Smith, F. Graham, *Radio Astronomy*. Penguin, 1960.

Individual Planets

†Alter, Dinsmore, ed., *Lunar Atlas*. Dover : Constable, 1966.

Baldwin, Ralph B., *The Measure of the Moon*. University of Chicago Press, 1963.

Bates, D. R., ed., *The Earth and Its Atmosphere*. Basic Books, New York, 1957.

Fraser, Ronald, *The Habitable Earth*, Hodder & Stoughton, 1965.

Kellogg, William W., and Carl Sagan, *The Atmospheres of Mars and Venus*. Publication 944, National Academy of Sciences-National Research Council, 1961.

Kendrew, Wilfred G., *Climatology* (2nd edition). Oxford University Press, 1957.

Kopal, Zdeněk, *The Moon: Our Nearest Celestial Neighbor* (2nd edition). Chapman & Hall, 1963.

Peek, Bertrand M., *The Planet Jupiter*. Faber, 1959.

*Spar, Jerome, *Earth, Sea, and Air*. Addison-Wesley, 1962.

Strahler, A. N., *The Earth Sciences*. Harper & Row, 1963.

Our Solar System

*Berkner, Lloyd N., and Hugh Odishaw, *Science in Space*. McGraw-Hill, 1961.

Jackson, Joseph H., *Pictorial Guide to the Planets*. Thomas Y. Crowell: Innes Rose, 1965.

Kuiper, G. P., and Barbara M. Middlehurst, eds., *Planets and Satellites*. University of Chicago Press, 1961.

Page, Thornton, and Lou Williams, eds., *Wanderers in the Sky*. Macmillan, 1965.

†Smith, Alexander G., and Thomas D. Carr, *Radio Exploration of the Planetary System*. Van Nostrand, 1964.

Whipple, Fred L., *Earth, Moon and Planets* (revised edition). Harvard : Oxford University Press, 1963.

*Also available in paperback edition.

†Only available in paperback edition.

ACKNOWLEDGEMENTS

The editors of this book are indebted to the following persons and institutions: Elso S. Barghoorn and I. William Schopf, Department of Biology, Harvard University, Cambridge; Glenn L. Berge, Owens Valley Radio Observatory, California Institute of Technology, Pasadena; Frank E. Bristow, Manager, News Bureau, Jet Propulsion Laboratory, Pasadena; Virginia Burton, The Metropolitan Museum of Art, New York City; Marshall Cohen, Department of Astronomy, Cornell University, Ithaca; Wendell C. DeMarcus, Physics Department, University of Kentucky, Lexington; John Dickel and Stanley Wyatt Jr., Department of Astronomy, University of Illinois, Urbana; Robert S. Dietz, U.S. Navy Electronics Laboratory, San Diego; James Edson, Dennis Evans, Paul Lowman and William Pommeroy, National Aeronautics and Space Administration, Washington, D.C.; Kenneth L. Franklin, Hayden Planetarium, New York City; Richard Goldstein, Jet Propulsion Laboratory, California Institute of Technology, Pasadena; Bruce Heezen, Lamont Geological Observatory, Palisades, N.Y.; Raymond Hide, Departments of Physics and of Geology and Geophysics, Massachusetts Institute of Technology, Cambridge; M.J.S. Innes, Department of Mines and Technical Surveys, Ottawa, Canada; Philip B. King, U.S. Geological Survey, Menlo Park, Calif.; Sarah Lee Lippincott, Sproul Observatory, Swarthmore College, Swarthmore, Pa.; Frank Low, Lunar and Planetary Laboratory, University of Arizona, Tucson; John Lutnes, Kitt Peak National Observatory, Tucson; James R. Miller and William Miller, California Institute of Technology, Pasadena; Harland Nasvik, General Mills, Inc., Minneapolis; Eugene M. Shoemaker, Chief, and Howard A. Pohn, Branch of Astrogeology, U.S. Geological Survey, Flagstaff, Ariz.; S. M. Siegel, Group Leader, Physical Biochemistry, Union Carbide Research Institute, Tarrytown, N.Y.; T. C. Southerland Jr., Department of Astrophysical Sciences, Princeton University, Princeton, N.J.; Arthur Strahler, Geology Department, Columbia University, New York City; John Strong, Research Contract Director, John McLellan, Donald McLeod and William Plummer, Laboratory of Astrophysics and Physical Meteorology, The Johns Hopkins University, Baltimore; and Homer Thompson, Institute for Advanced Study, Princeton, N.J.

INDEX

Numerals in italics indicate a photograph or illustration of the subject mentioned.

PICTURE CREDITS

The sources for the illustrations which appear in this book are shown below. Credits for the pictures from left to right are separated by commas, from top to bottom by dashes.

CHAPTER 1: 8—Courtesy Simone Gossner. 10—The Granger Collection. 11—Drawings by Nicholas Fasciano. 12—Courtesy Simone Gossner. 13—William C. Miller. 15—Culver Pictures—drawing by Donald and Ann Crews. 17 to 31—Drawings by Leo and Diane Dillon.

CHAPTER 2: 32—Howard Sochurek. 34—Drawings by Donald and Ann Crews from *Science and Civilization in China,* Vol. III, by Joseph Needham, courtesy Cambridge University Press. 35—Drawings by Donald and Ann Crews. 36—Drawing by Leslie Martin. 38—Drawing by Donald and Ann Crews. 39—Drawings by Leslie Martin. 41—William Schopf and Elso S. Barghoorn. 45—Drawings by Otto van Eersel. 46 to 49—NASA. 50, 51—Emil Schulthess from Black Sea—Ernst Haas from Magnum. 52, 53—Left Fritz Goro; centre Dmitri Kessel; right Dmitri Kessel—Andreas Feininger—Ralph Crane from Black Star. 54—Steven C. Wilson from Meridian Photos, Rene Burri from Magnum—Stan Wayman, A. Y. Owen—Nina Leen, A. Y. Owen. 55—Steven C. Wilson from Meridian Photos, Rene Burri from Magnum, Alfred Eisenstaedt—Dr. Roman Vishniac, Douglas Faulkner, Fritz Goro—Rene Burri from Magnum, Alfred Eisenstaedt, John Dominis, 56 to 59—Drawings by David Klein.

CHAPTER 3: 60—Walter Sanders courtesy Museo di Storia della Scienza, Florence. 62—The Granger Collection—courtesy Simone Gossner. 64, 65—Drawings by Nicholas Fasciano. 66, 67—Drawing by George V. Kelvin. 69—Derek Bayes. 70—Eric Schaal. 71—Wilson Hole Studios—Eric Schaal, Observatoire de Haute Provence. 72, 73—J. R. Eyerman. 74, 75—Laurence R. Lowry from Rapho Guillumette for FORTUNE, J. R. Eyerman, Arthur Siegel. 76, 77—J. R. Eyerman. 78, 79—Courtesy Johns Hopkins University. 80—Jet Propulsion Laboratory. 81—J. R. Eyerman.

CHAPTER 4: 82—A. Y. Owen. 84—Courtesy Museo di Storia della Scienza, Florence, 85—Vivarelli courtesy Biblioteca Nazionale, Rome—courtesy The Science Museum, London. 86, 87—Mount Wilson and Palomar Observatories Photograph—drawings by Nicholas Fasciano. 88, 89—Drawings by Nicholas Fasciano. 90—The Granger Collection. 93—Sovfoto. 95—Lick Observatory Photograph. 96—Lick Observatory Photograph courtesy North American Aviation, Inc. from *Lunar Atlas.* 97—Mount Wilson and Palomar Observatories Photograph courtesy North American Aviation, Inc. from *Lunar Atlas.* 98, 99—NASA. 100, 101—NASA. 102, 103—NASA. 104, 105—NASA. 106, 107—NASA.

CHAPTER 5: 108—Courtesy the Trustees of The British Museum. 114—Drawing by Donald and Ann Crews. 115—Drawings by Leslie Martin. 117—Drawings by Donald and Ann Crews. 119—Courtesy Simone Gossner. 120—Left E. C. Slipher, Lowell Observatory Photograph; right Lowell Observatory Photographs. 121, 122—Drawings by Otto van Eersel. 123—NASA. 124 to 129—Drawings by Paul Calle.

CHAPTER 6: 130—W. S. Finsen, Republic Observatory, Johannesburg. 132—Drawing by Donald and Ann Crews. 133—Courtesy Simone Gossner. 135—Drawing by Donald and Ann Crews. 137—The Bettmann Archive. 139—Drawing by Donald and Ann Crews. 141—Emmett Bright courtesy Biblioteca Estense. 142. 143—Left Osservatorio Astronòmico Di Brere; centre Lowell Observatory Photograph; right from *La Planete Mars* by E. M. Antoniadi, Librairie Scientifique Hermann except top Sovfoto. 144—Jet Propulsion Laboratory, California Institute of Technology, NASA. 145—NASA—Jet Propulsion Laboratory, California Institute of Technology, NASA. 146—Lowell Observatory Photographs. 147—Drawings by Nicholas Fasciano. 148 to 151—Drawings by Paul Calle.

CHAPTER 7: 152—Emmett Bright courtesy Museo di Storia della Scienza, Florence. 155—Drawings by Leslie Martin. 157—Drawing by Leslie Martin, adapted from *The Planet Jupiter* by B. M. Peek, courtesy Faber and Faber. 158—Drawings by George V. Kelvin. 161—California Institute of Technology and Carnegie Institution of Washington—drawing by Otto van Eersel. 162—Drawing by George V. Kelvin. 163—The Cook Observatory—drawings by Nicholas Fasciano. 164, 165—Drawing by Nicholas Fasciano—drawing by Paul Lehr. 166, 167—Drawing by David Klein.

CHAPTER 8: 168—C. J. Barnes, Goodyear Aerospace Corporation. 172, 173—Hubert C. Birnbaum courtesy Simone Gossner. 174, 175—Drawing by Otto van Eersel. 182, 183—Mount Wilson and Palomar Observatories Photographs except top right Yerkes Observatory Photograph University of Chicago, Lick Observatory Photograph University of California. 184, 185—Mount Wilson and Palomar Observatories Photographs. 186, 187—J. R. Eyerman courtesy Ames Research Center. 188—Ted Russell—Los Alamos Scientific Laboratory, University of California. 189—Union Carbide. 190, 191—Drawing by Paul Calle. 194—Drawings by George V. Kelvin.

XXXXX

Typesetting by C. E. Dawkins (Typesetters) Ltd., London, S.E.1
Smeets Lithographers, Weert, Printed in Holland
Bound by Proost en Brandt N.V., Amsterdam